LUCI

VERA HISTORIA

Ἀληθὴς Ἱστορία

TRUE HISTORY

THon.

LUCIANI
VERA HISTORIA

Ἀληθὴς Ἱστορία

Edited with

INTRODUCTION and NOTES

by

C.S. JERRAM, M.A.

ILLUSTRATIONS BY THOM KAPHEIM

Bolchazy-Carducci Publishers

Cover by Thom Kapheim

Reprint of the Edition
Oxford at the Claredon Press 1879

Bolchazy-Carducci Publishers
1000 Brown St.
Wauconda, IL 60084

Printed in the United States of America
International Standard Book Number
0-86516-240-9

1990 INTRODUCTION

True History is a unique ancient book whose influence on several modern genres is unmistakable. The Satirical Romance/ Travelogue, Science Fiction and The Tall Tale are three that come to mind immediately. Lucian's trip to the Moon and other environs of outer space is the oldest extant version to come down to us, though the idea of inhabited extraterrestrial worlds is a speculation of such Presocratic philosophers as Democritus and Leucippus. The story concludes with a reference to "another continent" on the other side of the globe, making *True History* a part of the Atlantis tradition in Western literature. The story of being swallowed by a large fish and inhabiting its belly has haunted scholars for ages because of its similarity to the Biblical Jonah legend.

Without Lucian's comic classic, there would be no *Somnium* by Joannes Kepler, *Voyages to the Empire of the Sun and the Moon* by Cyrano de Bergerac or *Gulliver's Travels* by Jonathan Swift. Erasmus, Thomas More and Voltaire were also highly influenced by the intellectual pyrotechnics of *True History.*

Readers will notice some of Lucian's tricks at once, such as the regular playful allusions to famous works of literature like Aristophanes' *The Birds* and Homer's *Odyssey.* There are jokes and puns of all sorts in addition to outrageous sexual fantasies that are very lighthearted in nature. As with Jonathan Swift, Lucian plays with the scale of things, producing impossible giants and monsters at every turn. There is nothing like Lucian's gigantic insects and spiders until modern science fiction. Many famous figures from Greek mythology—from the Minotaur to the Sirens—also reappear in the transmutated forms of alien creatures encountered in exotic lands beyond the ones we already know.

Perhaps *True History's* most challenging aspect is to be found in the interplay between truth and falsehood, suggesting that it is difficult for all people to avoid being victims of a Tall Tale. For a story whose author says from the outset that it is all make-believe, there is certainly a repeated harping on such themes as "I saw it with my own eyes" and "I know it sounds unbelievable, but it really happened." No less than Lucian's original readers, we remain confused over issues of credibility and veracity in our authorities, experts, professionals and eye-witnesses. Whom do we believe and why? And how much do we believe them? How far will we go before we realize someone is "pulling our leg"?

Despite the puns and literary allusions, *True History* is an easy reader for students and teachers of classical Greek. The style and diction are very similar to the early dialogues of Plato and a small *Liddell & Scott Lexicon* is sufficient support. Besides, there is such a youthful exuberance in this fabulous tale that modern readers of all ages will find it fun.

Casey Fredericks

July, 1990

PREFACE.

THE publication of this edition of Lucian's *Vera Historia* follows rather closely upon that of *Cebetis Tabula*, edited by me for the Clarendon Press Series a few months ago. Although these two works are widely different in character, my object in publishing them is in both cases the same; viz. to provide the student of Greek, in the earlier stages of his work, with a greater variety of material than he now has at his disposal. The fact that fewer boys now learn Greek than was formerly the case, substitution of 'modern' subjects being very generally allowed, is a reason why ampler provision should be made for those who do; since these may fairly be presumed to have some aptitude for the study and a desire to attain some proficiency in it. To get this result the interest of the pupil must be excited, not indeed at the expense of verbal accuracy or so as to avoid the necessary labour, but alongside of this and by way of an additional incentive to work. A loose style of translation, that secures the general sense of a passage but misses its grammatical construction, is not likely to be encouraged in these days of exact and even *ultra* refined scholarship; but the opposite fault, that of extreme literalness without any attempt at style, is very often committed. Having been necessarily taught all along to concentrate his attention upon the grammatical forms and constructions of the new language he is learning, a boy is apt to lose sight of the wholesome maxim that 'whatever makes nonsense must be *wrong;*' not perhaps wrong with respect to the rules of Latin or Greek syntax, of whose requirements he may be even painfully conscious, but as regards order and choice of words, arrangement of clauses, and all that tends to clearness of expression in his own native tongue, which he has never been taught properly to handle. Hence arises the common schoolboy notion that no absurdity of language is too great for a 'classical' writer to perpetrate, and that nonsense is rather to be expected than otherwise from one who appears to be so far removed from common every-day conditions. The best way of curing this misconception is to make sure that the pupil thoroughly understands the matter of the book he is translating, both as a whole and in its several parts; and this he will do the more readily, if it be of a nature to interest and even to amuse him. The *Vera Historia* of Lucian, now for the first time edited as a school-book, is eminently a work of this kind, being a romance of moderate length, full of marvellous adventures, that might well induce any boy who is making fair progress in Greek to read it for the sake of its contents alone. The labour involved would not be great; there are a certain number of unfamiliar words which would require looking out, but the constructions are quite easy, and framed as a rule upon the best Attic prose models. Older students also may well be interested in the perusal of one of the most ancient specimens of romance writing, when the art was yet in its infancy; they will mark the vivacity of style and pointedness of the satire, and trace the historical and mythological allusions with which the work abounds. In short the book is one that ought to be in every sense *popular*, and I put it forth as an experiment in the success of which I cannot help feeling some degree of confidence.

In dividing the text into sections, each with a descriptive heading, I have followed the plan adopted in the 'Easy Selections from Xenophon,' edited by Mr. Phillpotts and myself. This arrangement for young students has, I believe, met with very general approbation. I have not troubled about collation of MSS. and various readings, not having found any of particular importance, but have simply reprinted the chosen (Tauchnitz) text with only a few minor alterations.

CHARLES S. JERRAM.

Woodcote House School, Windlesham,
January, 1879

PREFACE TO THE SECOND EDITION.

THE present edition has undergone a thorough revision, and several fresh notes have been inserted, especially in the First Book, which was somewhat sparsely annotated in the former edition. The English of all words not to be found in Liddell and Scott's smaller Greek Lexicon is now given, some of them having previously escaped notice. The favourable reception hitherto accorded to the work in many schools induces the hope that it may ere long be generally adopted as a Second Greek reading-book, and any suggestions with a view to further improvements will be thankfully received.

C. S. J.

May, 1880

INTRODUCTION.

Sketch of Lucian's life and of his chief works. His attacks upon the religion, philosophy, and social follies of the day. The *Vera Historia* a romance with a purpose. Its probable sources. Lucian's attitude towards Christianity. His versatility of style. Modern imitations and translations of the *Vera Historia.*

THE author of the *Vera Historia* shares with many other illustrious writers the advantage or disadvantage of being in a sense his own biographer. In the absence of any trustworthy details of his life derivable from other sources we have to depend upon scattered notices to be found in his own works, and these afford at the best but meagre materials. The date of Lucian's birth has with some probability been assigned to the first quarter of the second century A. D., and there are reasons for believing that he lived nearly, if not quite, to the close of it, so that we may say he 'flourished' as a writer from A. D. 160–190. Born about 120 A. D. of humble parents, at Samosata in the Roman province of Commagene, he early found the necessity of being apprenticed to some calling by which he might gain a livelihood. After a council of relations and neighbours had debated the matter, he was, as he tells us, committed to the charge of his maternal uncle, a Mercury-carver of some repute, to be taught the craft and art of a statuary. But his first and only essay proved unfortunate; for whatever may have been his aptitude for modelling in wax, as manifested in his school-boy days, his hand now proved too heavy for his uncle's marble and temper. The slab broke[1], and the young sculptor re-

[1] As Dr. Dyer suggests, 'an omen of his future course . . . as an iconoclast.'

ceived the encouragement of a sound thrashing. To run away home and to pour out his griefs to his sympathising mother was his immediate resource; then going to bed he dreamed a dream that for the next five-and-twenty years was to shape his destiny. 'Two women methought laid violent hands upon me, each dragging me with all her force towards her;' one was 'hard-handed dusty Sculpture,' the other 'fair Eloquence[1].' In the sequel 'he flew with rapture to the latter, doubtless with the greater joy from the remembrance of the blows which he had received the day before,' and like Xenophon he tells us he has recorded his dream, because the relation of it might be useful to mankind and might persuade young men to follow literature. The choice of a sculptor's career, rather than one of the liberal professions, had, in Lucian's case, been originally made in great measure in consequence of the poverty of his parents, and how after this dream he was enabled to override this practical difficulty we are not told. From the dialogue entitled *Bis Accusatus* we gather that for some considerable time he wandered about Ionia, 'in habit little better than an Assyrian slave, in language a mere barbarian, and not knowing which way to turn himself.' Later on it appears that he became an advocate, though at first with but meagre success; and so, as a means of gain, to the practice of Jurisprudence he added that of Rhetoric, composing orations for others to deliver. If the short account in Suidas' Lexicon is to be trusted, Antioch was the scene of these early efforts. Thence he soon set out on his travels, and visited in due course Greece, Italy and Gaul, gradually attaining success, and making, especially in Gaul, the moderate fortune that at the age of forty enabled him once more to change his profession. He had, he says, grown weary of a calling sadly fallen since the days of Demosthenes, and was sick of the tricks and pretensions now characteristic of its professors. He returned home for awhile,

[1] Francklin's English version. But the original is Παιδεία, i. e. 'Education.' The Dream is evidently suggested by the apologue of the Choice of Hercules, delivered by Prodicus the sophist and recorded by Xenophon, *Memorabilia*, ii. 1.

and before migrating with his family (his father was still living) into Greece, he appears to have visited Alexander, the Paphlagonian prophet, at Aboniteichos, on the Euxine. His exposure of that arch-impostor is one of the most amusing of his works, and though certainly written at a much later time, when he had acquired that polished Attic style[1] that recals the best period of the language, it may be taken as incidentally recording an actual visit made about this date. Of the events of Lucian's later years we have scarcely any particulars. All we know is that he lived permanently at Athens, and devoted himself to philosophy and literature. There he became acquainted with the genial Demonax of Cyprus, many of whose witty sayings he has preserved in the piece bearing that philosopher's name.

Towards the close of his long life, already 'with one foot in Charon's boat,' he seems to have again become poor, and was in spite of his objections to the humiliating condition of one in dependence on patronage[2], glad to accept an official appointment at Alexandria. This office he was allowed to discharge by deputy, and lived for awhile upon its emoluments, probably still at Athens. Here he must have enjoyed some years of literary leisure, the fruit of which appears in the number and variety of his works. If we are to regard as genuine the almost certainly spurious *Apology*[3], he was careful to defend himself against what appeared at first sight a gross inconsistency. There is all the difference in the world, he is there made to contend, between holding a public office under government and being dependent upon private liberality and

[1] We find in Lucian few departures from the strict classic standard. His chief peculiarities are the use of the subjunctive for optative and *vice versâ* in dependent clauses, and of the pluperfect for the aorist; of μή for οὐ in direct negations, and of ὡς for ὥστε with the infinitive; also the employment of several words and phrases unknown in earlier Attic Greek. See observations on these in the notes as they occur.

[2] Lucian had previously written an essay, *De Mercede Conductis*, setting forth (after the manner of Juvenal's 5th Satire) the miseries of such dependence.

[3] *Apologia pro Mercede Conductis*, purporting to be a defence made by Lucian of his conduct in accepting this appointment.

individual caprice. Of the place or circumstances of his death nothing is known. Suidas assigns him a death by hydrophobia, but manifestly on the ground that nothing is too bad for a 'blasphemer;' a *sobriquet* that only too readily attached itself to one who in his keen hatred of imposture and superstition spared neither friend nor foe. The date of his death is also unknown, but 200 A.D. is probably not very far wide of the mark.

Lucian's works, representing a literary career of over forty years, are reckoned at eighty-two in all. Of these however fully one half have, by one critic or another, been rejected as spurious, often on very slender grounds, though that some of them are so there can be no reasonable doubt. Of the genuine pieces by far the larger proportion are *satires*, professed or involved, and indeed all have more or less of this element. Lucian, like Persius, was 'a great laugher with a saucy spleen[1],' and heartily hated all kinds of imposture or what he thought to be such. His ridicule was unsparing, not from mere love of hard hitting and buffoonery, but from a sincere desire to abolish the deception. Roughly speaking, his satire is directed against (1) the popular creed, (2) the professors of philosophy, (3) the vices and follies of society. It is not pretended that any such division is intentionally observed by him, or that his works can always be assigned to one or other of these heads; on the contrary, many pieces occupy a kind of border-land, and in the majority the religious element is found. The above will however be a convenient grouping for us to adopt in our necessarily brief survey.

Of the first kind the chief specimens are found in the *Dialogues of the Gods* and *Dialogues of the Dead*. The former are a series of burlesque pieces, ridiculing the time-honoured objects of popular devotion and a faith now fast growing obsolete. The very fact of Lucian daring to write them proves how completely the age of belief had given place to an age of enquiry. Time was when Plato ran the risk of giving serious offence to his more orthodox fellow-citizens, because he ob-

[1] Persius, *Sat.* i. 12, 'sed sum petulanti splene cachinno' (Conington's translation).

jected to the Homeric stories being taught to children on the ground of their immorality[1]; when Socrates amongst other charges was arraigned for asserting that 'the sun was a stone and the moon earth[2].' But these dialogues of Lucian are evidence of an altered state of things indeed. It is no longer a matter for argument, but for undisguised burlesque. The gods are 'of the earth, earthy,' and he treats them accordingly, taking the stories of their doings as literal facts and building his grotesque scenes out of materials ready prepared to his hand.

The *Dialogues of the Dead*, in spite of a display of ribaldry that is often outrageous, are marked nevertheless by a distinct seriousness of purpose. In them such subjects as the levelling of all estates of men after death and the final award of judgment are treated with a deep moral earnestness, which their cynical levity of form only serves to heighten by contrast. As instances we may cite the doom of the tyrant Megapenthes in the *Cataplus*[3], and the scene in the tenth dialogue, in which Charon's intending passengers in their several stations are forced to strip themselves of all that in life they had held most dear. These and other like specimens are admirably translated in Mr. Collins' 'Ancient Classics' series, whose *Lucian* should be in the hands of every student.

There is much in all these dialogues to prompt the feeling that, in spite of the delicacy of his literary skill and his keen appreciation of art, especially pictorial[4], Lucian was not a man of much real refinement. At any rate he wholly failed to appreciate the undertone which modern students of mythology have seemed to detect of the longings of humanity in even the rudest forms of religious faith. With him to destroy

[1] *Republic*, Book ii. Admitting the possibility of explaining some of these legends allegorically, Plato objects to this mode of interpretation for children, since they cannot distinguish allegory from matter of fact.

[2] *Apologia Socratis*, ch. xiv, τὸν μὲν ἥλιον λίθον φησὶν εἶναι, τὴν δὲ σελήνην γῆν. That this charge was false is conclusively shown in the *Defence*.

[3] See notes 1, 2 on p. xiv.

[4] See for instance the graphic description of the procession of Europa in the 15th of his *Marine Dialogues*.

was the principal aim, and ridicule his most potent weapon. And in this field we must fain allow that Lucian stands almost without a rival. The amours of Zeus, the jealousy of Hera, the gods dining out with 'blameless Ethiopians'[1] when most urgently required at home: the whole paraphernalia of Hades, with Charon's leaky boat and Hermes herding his shades, some of whom naturally try to escape if they can[2]; the Olympian council with its motley crowd of divinities all jostling for places, and Zeus at his wits' end to quell the disorder he has been unable to prevent[3],—above all the actual neglect of divine worship among mankind being urged as a taunt of weakness and imbecility against the 'King of gods and men'[4]—what Pantheon that ever existed, let alone one already tottering to its fall, could outlive such onslaughts as these?

But if Lucian is unsparing in his attacks upon the worn-out theology of his day, he deals not a whit more tenderly with the Philosophers and Rhetoricians. He never loses a chance of girding at them, and in the *Sale of Lives* (Βίων Πρᾶσις) especially he indulges in many scurrilous jokes at their expense. Even such men as Pythagoras and Socrates do not escape, nor does Diogenes, in spite of the author's real regard for him, fare much better. Like Aristophanes, who ridiculed Socrates in the *Clouds*, Lucian must be allowed to have his jest at any price. There can be little doubt that the real object of his satire was not genuine philosophy, but the wretched imposture that the philosophical profession had become in his day. He hated with a perfect hatred the host of ignorant pretenders, who traded on the reputation of their (supposed) masters, and were as immoral as they were ignorant. He introduced the great names of antiquity[5] less as

[1] *Prometheus*, § 17 (from Homer, *Il.* i. 423). This and some of the other pieces referred to, though not ranked among the *Deorum* and *Mortuorum Dialogi*, are of the same character, and illustrate a similar intention on the part of the author.

[2] *Cataplus*, or the 'Downward Voyage,' referred to above.

[3] *Deorum Concilium*, also *Jupiter Tragoedus* (which some consider spurious).

[4] *Timon*. See 'Ancient Classics,' *Lucian*, pp. 41, etc.

[5] In the *Piscator* Lucian is triumphantly acquitted of bearing any *animus* against genuine philosophers.

individuals than as well-known representatives of the various sects or classes which he designed to caricature. In the ridicule he casts upon the teachers of Rhetoric and Dialectic we cannot but feel that Lucian is speaking from his own experience in early life, and he certainly displays an admirable courage in thus assailing them. For in his time these men were exceedingly popular, and to try and expose them and put them down was a far more hazardous proceeding than to attack an already discredited Olympus. The sort of hornet's nest that he would be likely to bring about him is scarcely exaggerated in the amusing dialogue known as *Piscator*, where he represents himself as pursued by a host of angry philosophers, all thirsting for revenge and united in one common cause for their enemy's destruction.

Of Lucian's *social* satire it may be said with Juvenal (i. 85, 86):

> 'Quicquid agunt homines, votum timor ira voluptas
> Gaudia discursus, nostri est farrago libelli.'

Almost all his dialogues contain specimens of it, and it is the distinct purpose of several separate pieces. Among these, that entitled the *Parasite* is the defence of his trade by a professional 'diner-out.' His arguments are a fair imitation of the conversational style of Socrates, and some of them are not altogether without force. It is, he contends, a real *art*, and one pleasing to host and guest alike, and what can be more 'genteel'? Great men of all ages have held it in high esteem and practised it. The *De Mercede Conductis* (which we have already noticed) sets forth in the form of a letter the miseries of 'hired dependents,' and is directed against those contemptible philosophical and literary hacks, whom the fashion of the day made an indispensable appendage to every family of position. It is not so very long since that the sting of the piece would have been felt even in England, and Francklin, who wrote about one hundred years ago, introduces his translation of it to his readers with the remark that it affords 'very good lessons to all the led captains, toad-eaters, and domestic tutors of the present age.'

But there was another folly that specially stirred Lucian's anger; superstition and an insane craving for the 'sensational' and the marvellous. With this subject he deals in some three or four pieces, and notably in the *Philopseudes* or 'Lover of Lies.' Here we have ghosts, 'bogies,' and horrible apparitions *ad nauseam;* sympathetic cures, walking statues, a pestle that would fetch water and do menial work; a view of the infernal regions, and messages from the spirit-world. Lucian sufficiently marks his contempt for these absurdities by calling the retailer of them 'a jackanapes in a lion's skin[1],' or else a raving lunatic.

The *Vera Historia* or 'Veracious History' belongs to the same class as the *Philopseudes*, but is cast in the form of a romance. In its main outline it is an avowed satire on the tales of professed poets and historians, some of whom are mentioned by name; and Lucian makes it his boast that he can hold his own in the art of lying with any of them. So naturally and with such an air of reality is the story told, that in his preface he finds it necessary to guard the credulous amongst his readers from being misled, by warning them that 'the only word of truth in the whole is the confession that I mean to lie.'

The contents of the piece are sufficiently indicated by the headings of the sections of the text in this edition, and need not here be anticipated. Its form, that of an imaginary voyage, is an obvious and convenient one for stringing together a number of adventures having no particular connexion with each other. According to Photius the story is imitated from an account of the Wonders of the Island of Thule by Antiochus Diogenes, who lived in the time of Alexander the Great. Of that work only the extracts given by Photius remain, and if these are fair samples of the whole, our author has certainly improved upon his model in regard to the marvellous element. For while the fictions of Lucian are only occasional distortions of some ascertained fact[2], those of Antiochus are much more frequently so.

[1] *Philopseudes*, § 5. ἆρα τοσοῦτον χρόνον ἐλελήθει με ὑπὸ τῇ λεοντῇ γελοῖόν τινα πίθηκον περιστέλλων. [2] See notes on i. 359, ii. 33.

But to speculate on all the possible originals of Lucian's romance is useless. A start being once made, imagination would do the rest; we shall therefore only indicate a few of the obvious or most probable sources of allusion. These are chiefly Homer's Odyssey, certain stories in Herodotus (mentioned in the notes to this edition), and the Indian History of Ctesias[1] named in Lucian's preface. To these may be added the work of Iambulus[2], of which the account given by Diodorus Siculus is said to be an epitome. But besides these Greek sources there are plain traces of Indian fable. Not only had Lucian been a great traveller in his youth, but the place of his birth, situated as it was upon the confines of the Eastern and Western world, may well have made him familiar with Oriental tales. The stories in the collection known as the Arabian Nights are some of them very ancient, or at least founded on very ancient traditions, and there are at any rate two incidents in the *Vera Historia* that may have been borrowed from this source. The similarity between the gigantic Kingfisher (ii. 560) and the Roc, or Rukh, that in the Second Voyage of Sinbad the Sailor 'alighted on the dome [its egg] and brooded over it with its wings'[3] is obvious. Again in the Fifth Voyage the sailors break the Roc's egg and eat the young one which they find inside[4]. The only doubt indeed arises from the sequel of this tale in the Arabian Nights. There the ship is smashed by the enraged birds in revenge for their broken egg, and the temptation to note this incident would scarcely, we think, have been resisted by Lucian, if he had heard of it. The counterpart to the huge sea monster (i. 448) appears in a story told (not in the text of the Thousand and One Nights), but in the Cairo edition of Sinbad's Seventh Voyage[5]. In this expedition they encounter an enormous fish that could gulp down ships with their crews entire, and Sinbad's vessel would have been thus swallowed, had not a storm come on and broken it in pieces just at the critical moment.

[1] See note on i. 22. [2] i. 25, note. [3] Lane's translation.
[4] Cp. *V. H.* ii. 572. [5] Lane's edition, vol. iii. p. 109.

In Lucian's description of the City of the Blest[1] and its surroundings the imagery of the East and of the West combine. The gold and precious stones, the river of unguents, and the spice-perfumed baths are 'properties' as surely Oriental as the meads and groves, the zephyrs and fountains, the flowery couches and musical birds of the Elysian Field are unmistakably Greek. Whence the Eastern element in his picture was derived opens up a question that has been much debated. Even a cursory reader cannot fail to observe, notably in the vines that yield their fruit every month and in the great altars all of one huge amethyst, a striking similarity to the description of the New Jerusalem in the Apocalypse. But was Lucian acquainted with the Christian literature? No *proof* of this exists, and the balance of evidence appears to us to point in a contrary direction. The distinctly anti-Christian dialogue *Philopatris* was written possibly by a namesake who corresponded with the Emperor Julian, but was certainly not the work of the author of the *Vera Historia*. In his account of some religious rites practised by the false prophet Alexander, he does indeed mention the Christians, and in connexion too with 'atheists and Epicureans;' but this classification is not Lucian's own, but that of the impostor's admirers[2], who warn unbelievers of every class to keep aloof from their pretended mysteries. Here therefore there is no evidence that our author intended to cast any slur upon the Christians, but rather the contrary. To their sacred books he makes no certain allusion of any kind, nor are there any passages in his works that necessarily indicate the slightest familiarity with them. The only other mention[3] of the Christians, by name is in the *Peregrinus*. This work we incline to believe is Lucian's, though there have not been want-

[1] ii. 145, etc.

[2] The words of the proclamation are, Εἴ τις ἄθεος ἢ Χριστιανὸς ἢ Ἐπικούρειος ἥκει κατάσκοπος τῶν ὀργίων φευγέτω· οἱ δὲ πιστεύοντες τῷ θεῷ τελείσθωσαν τύχῃ τῇ ἀγαθῇ.

[3] In the *Philopseudes* he speaks of 'a Syrian from Palestine' who cast out devils; but, as Mr. Collins points out, we know from the Acts that there were professed exorcists who were not Christians.

ing critics of mark who have rejected it. Herein, we must allow, Lucian does ridicule certain practices of the Christians, which he may well have thought 'marvellous'[1]; but he does so only incidentally, as it were, and not with malice. To regard the whole piece as a satire on the martyrdom of Polycarp or any other Christian, is to lose sight of the fact that the main circumstances of the account are recorded by Church writers themselves, and also to misunderstand the intention of the author. His object was not to denounce the Christian or any existing form of religion, but to hold up to derision that charlatanism and imposture of which Peregrinus was so conspicuous an example. That in his castigation the Christians were also in some measure involved was hardly Lucian's fault, since it was their countenancing the man that alone brought them even incidentally upon the scene[2]. Probably Lucian troubled himself little about this 'new superstition' (as he doubtless considered it)—to him it was at any rate far less obnoxious than the paganism which he set himself to denounce, and of its real nature he nowhere gives reason to suppose that he had any adequate conception. A certain outside acquaintance with the more prominent doctrines and practices of the Christian brotherhood is all that can fairly be claimed for him. We must therefore hesitate to conclude that Lucian's picture of the City of the Blest is founded, even in part, on that of the New Jerusalem in the Revelation; and any resemblance that may be detected between them is evidence only of a recourse to that common storehouse of Oriental imagery, with its gold and precious stones and all the accessories of barbaric splendour, whence the details of both descriptions were undoubtedly derived[3].

[1] *Τὴν θαυμαστὴν σοφίαν τῶν Χριστιανῶν.* *Peregrinus*, § 11.

[2] According to Lucian's account Peregrinus seems to have joined the Christians with the express design of profiting by their simplicity. They regarded him as a great prophet, 'almost as a god,' allowing him to comment upon, and even to interpolate, their sacred books. During his imprisonment they subscribed liberally for his support, so that he very soon became a rich man (*πρόσοδον οὐ μικρὰν ταύτην ἐκτήσατο*).

[3] Some keen-sighted commentators have even detected in the sea-monster, the chasm in the ocean (ii. 610), and the blossoming of the

The *Veracious History* is then a romance with a purpose such as we have described; but although its satire is chiefly directed against the poets and historians who are its avowed object, Lucian does not stop here. He turns upon the philosophers also, and burlesques them and their opinions with a zest that reminds us of some of his earlier essays[1]. Indeed some have esteemed those sections of the Second Book which deal with this subject the best part of his work: certainly his treatment of the various philosophical schools is full of elegance and point, and moreover is fairly free from exaggeration. Socrates and his tiresome cross-questionings, Plato dwelling apart in his self-constituted Utopia, Pythagoras unrecognisable after his manifold transmigrations, Academic doubts and Stoic pertinacity, are made, each in turn, to serve the purpose of the satirist. In another place he holds up to ridicule the really absurd notion of the dead performing bodily functions and being influenced by human emotions[2], noting too the hopeless confusion in the popular creed concerning the nether world, between the lifeless *body* and the semi-material *shade*, as if what affected the one must needs affect the other also[3]. The chief fault of the work is an exuberance of invention, and a too rapid transition from one marvel to another. Just as a conjuror's tricks, following each other in rapid succession, at last seem quite natural and make us forget the difficulty of the performance, so Lucian's prodigies tend by overcrowding to sate the imagination, and fail to impress it with an uniform sense of wonder. This effect is however in a great measure counteracted by the life-like picturesqueness of his style, which enables him to relate the wildest absurdities as though they were matters of daily oc-

mast (ii. 579), allusions to Jonah's 'great fish,' the passage of the Red Sea, and the budding of Aaron's rod respectively!

[1] Such as the *Sale of Lives* and the *Piscator* (if genuine) referred to on pp. xiv, xv.

[2] As in the case of Ulysses, Menelaus, Helen, Achilles, etc.

[3] See ii. 157, etc. Also in the *Dialogues of the Dead* (not to mention other instances) the money put into the mouth of the corpse is Charon's fare for conveying the shade, and Mausolus in Hades is said to be burdened by the weight of his marble tombstone.

currence. The *naturalness* of his story-telling imposes on the mind of the reader and leads it captive; soon we grow so much interested in the tale as to forget its egregious impossibility [1]. If he at times travels too fast, he never allows himself to fall into the opposite and more serious fault of loitering. From one marvel to another he pushes on, and keeps one's expectation ever on the *qui vive*. The diversity of his fiction, the rapid change from the hideous to the agreeable, his playful humour and continual strokes of satire (recalling perpetually the professions of his preface), the absence of all effort—this, with much besides, makes the *Veracious History* something more than a mere light piece for an idle hour, and commends it to readers of discrimination and taste. Some of the allusions have unavoidably lost their force of application, others are obscure, and a few quite irrecoverable. Still it is remarkable how much of the work, even as a satire, in spite of the distance of time and the difference of interests in the present day, applies itself to modern conditions. Travellers now, as formerly, bring home strange reports and tell fibs too, many modern customs are by no means invulnerable, wild literary and scientific theories are still broached, the battle still rages about the 'Homeric question,' discussion still goes on about 'the nature of the soul' and its state after death. Of course some acquaintance with what has been said by ancient historians and philosophers is presupposed in the student of a book like this, but that being taken for granted, we may with but slight reservation adopt the opinion of Tooke [2] that 'the satire is everywhere intelligible, because it is everywhere applicable.'

Among modern satires and romances the following have been mentioned by various writers as more or less suggested by Lucian's *Vera Historia*;—the *Visions* of Quevedo, De Bergerac's *Voyage to the Moon* and *Empire of the Sun*, Voltaire's

[1] Lucian's skill in this respect may be advantageously compared with the best efforts of Edgar Poe and his partial imitator Jules Verne. The array of mock science at the command of these writers made their attainment of *vraisemblance* very much easier.

[2] One of Lucian's translators. See p. xxiii.

Princess of Babylon and *Micromegas*, the *Gargantua*, etc. of Rabelais, Swift's *Gulliver*, and the renowned *Baron Münchhausen.*

With regard to the first of these, beyond the bare descriptions of Hell and the Last Judgment, and a general satire upon poets, historians, and pretenders to science and philosophy, there is scarcely anything that suggests a comparison with Lucian's work. Cyrano de Bergerac may very likely have borrowed from it both the general idea of his romance and one or two particulars, e. g. the notion of the inhabitants of the moon being nourished by smell, and odours inhaled taking the place of food. The greater part of his work is a burlesque on the natural philosophy of the day. Voltaire's *Micromegas* describes a voyage to the planet Saturn by an inhabitant of the Dog-star, who is afterwards conveyed to Jupiter on a comet and thence to the Earth on an Aurora Borealis. In the *Princess of Babylon* there is an account of a tribe called the Gangaridae, who harness unicorns in battle. With these they fight against the King of India, whose ten thousand elephants are pierced through and through by their horns. Rabelais may have taken the idea of his Lychnobii from the Lychnopolis of Lucius (see i. 406 note), but in our opinion not much besides. Swift's satire on the philosophers of Laputa may be compared *mutatis mutandis* with Lucian's; still there are no traces of direct imitation. In the preface it is said: 'The author was so distinguished for his *veracity*, that it became a sort of proverb among his neighbours, whenever anyone asserted a thing, to say, *it was as true as if Mr. Gulliver had spoken it.*' This may remind us of Lucian's mock professions of veracity, which occur once or twice in the *Vera Historia* [1]; an observation that applies also to the Münchhausen romance, in which the Baron harps perpetually on his alleged reputation for truthfulness and the credibility of his narrative. This of course is an ordinary common-place of marvel-mongers, and of itself proves nothing as to the source of any particular fiction; but a great many of Münchhausen's adventures are taken bodily, almost *totidem verbis*, from the

[1] See, for instance, i. 368, ii. 440.

Veracious History. In one chapter we are told how a hurricane carries the ship up into the moon, where are 'Vulture-riders' who figure in a war with the inhabitants of the sun. Their weapons are asparagus darts and mushroom shields. They have one finger on each hand and removable heads and eyes. Instead of dying in the ordinary way they dissolve into smoke. Afterwards we read of an island of cheese in a sea of milk, and an enormous kingfisher's nest, exactly as in Lucian. A sea-monster swallows up ship and crew entire. They find many nations inside him, and escape at last by propping open his mouth with masts. In all this there is obviously no originality on the author's part, but whether the other writers we have mentioned (except De Bergerac) were conscious imitators of Lucian is a question which will bear discussion.

One of Thackeray's *Sketches* is a caricature representing 'Clio the Muse of History supported by the Veracious Historians.' These are Homer, Virgil, Tasso, Rollin and others, in company with Münchhausen and Don Quixote. If Mr. Thackeray had remembered the *Vera Historia*, he might very well have given Lucian a place among them.

Of the translations of Lucian, which are not very numerous, we may mention, first and foremost, the German version by Wieland. There is one in English by 'Eminent Hands,' published in 1711, and another by Tooke, to which we have already referred. Francklin's translation in four volumes, 1781, is spirited and generally accurate, and may be reckoned the best in our language. In French the *Vera Historia* has been separately rendered by Godard de Beauchamp in his *Bibliothèque des Romans Grecs* (1746), and by Etienne Béquet in the *Collection des Romans Grecs*, published by Didot at Paris in 1823. There is also an adaptation of the piece for 'readers young and old,' published at Halle in 1876, by R. Schönborn, with six illustrations, entitled *Der Griechische Münchhausen, ein Lügen-märchen*. This is very nearly as entertaining as the original, and all who read German will find it worth their perusal.

The text of the present edition is that of the Tauchnitz Classics, by C. H. Weise, with some corrections of spelling and punctuation.

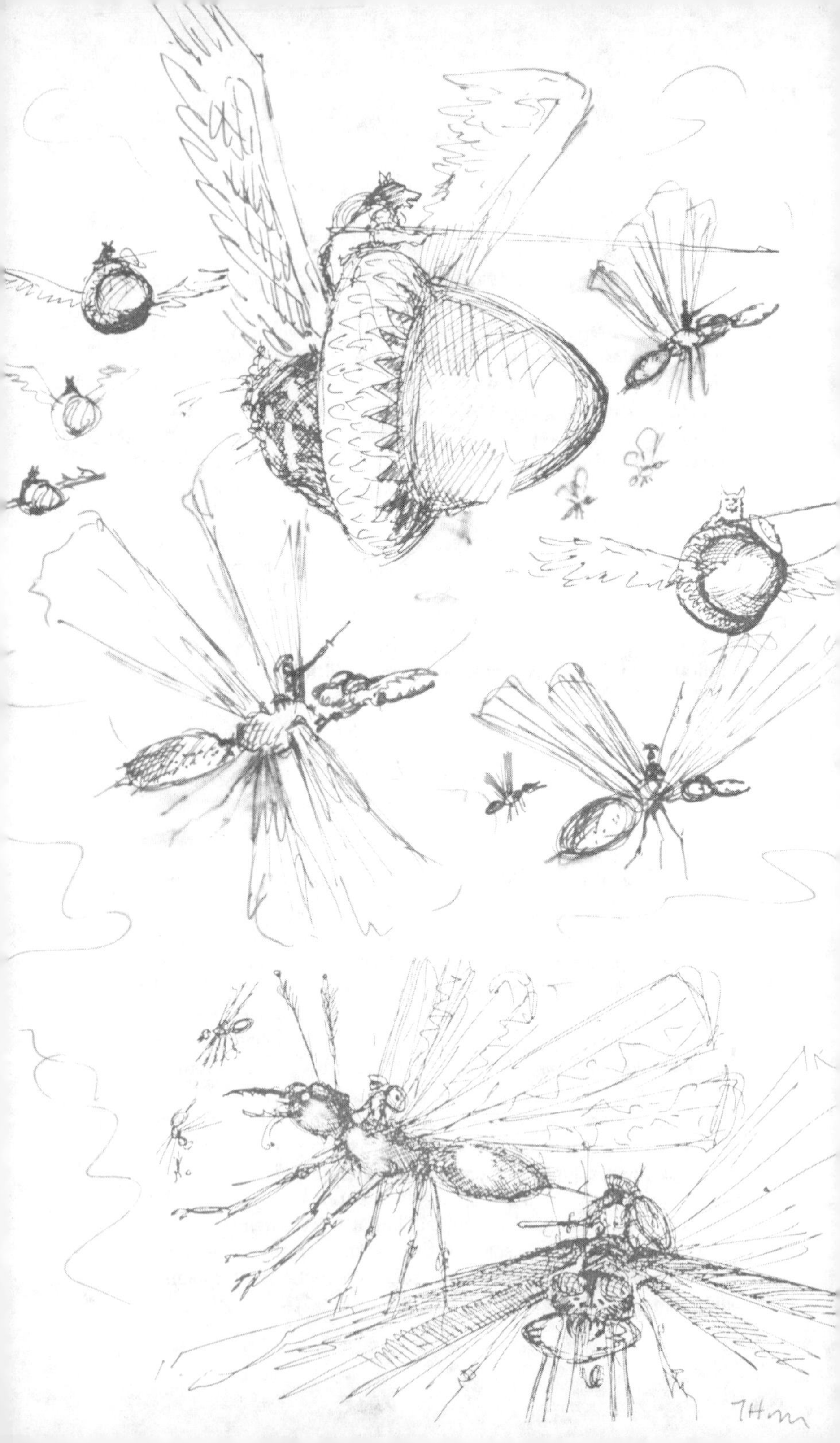

LUCIANI

VERA HISTORIA.

BOOK I.

Design of the work. 'The mind needs relaxation as well as the body, and light reading affords a relief from serious studies. Such is the design of the following story, which is not only entertaining in itself, but is expressly intended as a parody on the narratives of well-known poets and historians. These (with Homer at their head) have related many impossible marvels with an air of truth; I on the contrary give fair warning that my story is a pure fiction from beginning to end.'

Ὥσπερ τοῖς ἀθλητικοῖς καὶ περὶ τὴν τῶν σωμάτων ἐπιμέλειαν ἠσκημένοις οὐ τῆς εὐεξίας μόνον οὐδὲ τῶν γυμνασίων φροντίς ἐστιν, ἀλλὰ καὶ τῆς κατὰ καιρὸν γιγνομένης ἀνέσεως, μέρος γοῦν τῆς ἀσκήσεως τὸ μέγιστον αὐτὴν ὑπολαμβάνουσιν· οὕτω δὴ καὶ τοῖς περὶ λόγους 5 ἐσπουδακόσιν ἡγοῦμαι προσήκειν μετὰ τὴν πολλὴν τῶν σπουδαιοτέρων ἀνάγνωσιν, ἀνιέναι τε τὴν διάνοιαν καὶ πρὸς τὸν ἔπειτα κάματον ἀκμαιοτέραν παρασκευάζειν. γένοιτο δ' ἂν ἐμμελὴς ἡ ἀνάπαυσις αὐτοῖς, εἰ τοῖς τοιούτοις τῶν ἀναγνωσμάτων ὁμιλοῖεν, ἃ μὴ μόνον ἐκ τοῦ 10 ἀστείου τε καὶ χαρίεντος ψιλὴν παρέξει τὴν ψυχαγωγίαν, ἀλλά τινα καὶ θεωρίαν οὐκ ἄμουσον ἐπιδείξεται. οἷόν τι καὶ περὶ τῶνδε τῶν συγγραμμάτων φρονήσειν

ὑπολαμβάνω. οὐ γὰρ μόνον τὸ ξένον τῆς ὑποθέσεως,
15 οὐδὲ τὸ χάριεν τῆς προαιρέσεως ἐπαγωγὸν ἔσται αὐτοῖς,
οὐδ' ὅτι ψεύσματα ποικίλα πιθανῶς τε καὶ ἐναλήθως
ἐξενηνόχαμεν, ἀλλ' ὅτι καὶ τῶν ἱστορουμένων ἕκαστον
οὐκ ἀκωμῳδήτως πρός τινας ᾔνικται τῶν παλαιῶν ποιητῶν τε καὶ συγγραφέων καὶ φιλοσόφων, πολλὰ τερά-
20 στια καὶ μυθώδη συγγεγραφότων· οὓς καὶ ὀνομαστὶ ἂν
ἔγραφον, εἰ μὴ καὶ αὐτῷ σοι ἐκ τῆς ἀναγνώσεως φαίνεσθαι ἔμελλον. Κτησίας ὁ Κτησιόχου, ὁ Κνίδιος, συνέγραψε περὶ τῆς Ἰνδῶν χώρας καὶ τῶν παρ' αὐτοῖς, ἃ
μήτε αὐτὸς εἶδε μήτε ἄλλου εἰπόντος ἤκουσεν. ἔγραψε
25 δὲ καὶ Ἰαμβοῦλος περὶ τῶν ἐν τῇ μεγάλῃ θαλάττῃ πολλὰ παράδοξα· γνώριμον μὲν ἅπασι τὸ ψεῦδος πλασά-
μενος, οὐκ ἀτερπῆ δὲ ὅμως συνθεὶς τὴν ὑπόθεσιν. πολλοὶ δὲ καὶ ἄλλοι τὰ αὐτὰ τούτοις προελόμενοι συνέγρα-
ψαν, ὡς δή τινας ἑαυτῶν πλάνας τε καὶ ἀποδημίας θη-
30 ρίων τε μεγέθη ἱστοροῦντες, καὶ ἀνθρώπων ὠμότητας
καὶ βίων καινότητας. ἀρχηγὸς δὲ αὐτοῖς καὶ διδάσκαλος
τῆς τοιαύτης βωμολοχίας ὁ τοῦ Ὁμήρου Ὀδυσσεύς, τοῖς
περὶ τὸν Ἀλκίνοον διηγούμενος ἀνέμων τε δουλείαν καὶ
μονοφθάλμους καὶ ὠμοφάγους καὶ ἀγρίους τινὰς ἀν-
35 θρώπους· ἔτι δὲ πολυκέφαλα ζῶα καὶ τὰς ὑπὸ φαρμά-
κων τῶν ἑταίρων μεταβολάς· οἷα πολλὰ ἐκεῖνος πρὸς
ἰδιώτας ἀνθρώπους ἐτερατεύσατο τοὺς Φαίακας. τούτοις οὖν ἐντυχὼν ἅπασι τοῦ ψεύσασθαι μὲν οὐ σφόδρα
τοὺς ἄνδρας ἐμεμψάμην, ὁρῶν ἤδη σύνηθες ὂν τοῦτο
40 καὶ τοῖς φιλοσοφεῖν ὑπισχνουμένοις· ἐκεῖνο δ' αὐτῶν
ἐθαύμασα, εἰ ἐνόμισαν λήσειν οὐκ ἀληθῆ συγγράφοντες.
διόπερ καὶ αὐτὸς ὑπὸ κενοδοξίας ἀπολιπεῖν τι σπουδάσας
τοῖς μεθ' ἡμᾶς, ἵνα μὴ μόνος ἄμοιρος ὦ τῆς ἐν τῷ
μυθολογεῖν ἐλευθερίας, ἐπεὶ μηδὲν ἀληθὲς ἱστορεῖν εἶχον,

(οὐδὲν γὰρ ἐπεπόνθειν ἀξιόλογον) ἐπὶ τὸ ψεῦδος ἐτρα- 45
πόμην, πολλῷ τῶν ἄλλων εὐγνωμονέστερον. κἂν ἓν
γὰρ δὴ τοῦτο ἀληθεύσω λέγων, ὅτι ψεύσομαι· οὕτω
δ' ἄν μοι δοκῶ καὶ τὴν παρὰ τῶν ἄλλων κατηγορίαν
ἐκφυγεῖν, αὐτὸς ὁμολογῶν μηδὲν ἀληθὲς λέγειν. γράφω
τοίνυν περὶ ὧν μήτ' εἶδον, μήτε παρ' ἄλλων ἐπυθόμην· 50
ἔτι δὲ μήτε ὅλως ὄντων μήτε τὴν ἀρχὴν γενέσθαι
δυναμένων. διὸ δεῖ τοὺς ἐντυγχάνοντας μηδαμῶς πιστεύειν αὐτοῖς.

We start on our voyage and sail westward. After a violent storm, lasting many days, we are thrown upon an island.

Ὁρμηθεὶς γάρ ποτε ἀπὸ Ἡρακλείων στηλῶν καὶ
ἀφεὶς ἐς τὸν ἑσπέριον ὠκεανὸν οὐρίῳ ἀνέμῳ τὸν πλοῦν 55
ἐποιούμην. αἰτία δέ μοι τῆς ἀποδημίας καὶ ὑπόθεσις
ἡ τῆς διανοίας περιεργία καὶ πραγμάτων καινῶν ἐπι-
θυμία, καὶ τὸ βούλεσθαι μαθεῖν, ὅ τι τὸ τέλος ἐστὶ τοῦ
ὠκεανοῦ καὶ τίνες οἱ πέραν κατοικοῦντες ἄνθρωποι.
τούτου γέ τοι ἕνεκα πάμπολλα μὲν σιτία ἐνεβαλόμην, 60
ἱκανὸν δὲ καὶ ὕδωρ ἐνεθέμην, πεντήκοντα δὲ τῶν ἡλικιω-
τῶν προσεποιησάμην τὴν αὐτὴν ἐμοὶ γνώμην ἔχοντας·
ἔτι δὲ καὶ ὅπλων πολύ τι πλῆθος παρεσκευασάμην, καὶ
κυβερνήτην τὸν ἄριστον μισθῷ μεγάλῳ πείσας παρέ-
λαβον, καὶ τὴν ναῦν (ἄκατος δὲ ἦν) ὡς πρὸς μέγαν καὶ 65
βίαιον πλοῦν ἐκρατυνάμην. ἡμέραν μὲν οὖν καὶ νύκτα
οὐρίῳ ἀνέμῳ πλέοντες, ἔτι τῆς γῆς ὑποφαινομένης, οὐ
σφόδρα βιαίως ἀνηγόμεθα· τῇ ἐπιούσῃ δὲ ἅμα ἡλίῳ
ἀνίσχοντι ὅ τε ἄνεμος ἐπεδίδου καὶ τὸ κῦμα ηὐξάνετο
καὶ ζόφος ἐπεγίγνετο, καὶ οὐκέτ' οὐδὲ στεῖλαι τὴν ὀθόνην 70
δυνατὸν ἦν. ἐπιτρέψαντες οὖν τῷ πνεύματι καὶ παρα-
δόντες αὑτοὺς ἐχειμαζόμεθα ἡμέρας ἐννέα καὶ ἑβδομή-

κοντα· τῇ ὀγδοηκοστῇ δὲ, ἄφνω ἐκλάμψαντος ἡλίου, καθορῶμεν οὐ πόρρω νῆσον ὑψηλὴν καὶ δασεῖαν, οὐ τραχεῖ
75 περιηχουμένην τῷ κύματι· καὶ γὰρ ἤδη τὸ πολὺ τῆς ζάλης κατεπέπαυτο. προσσχόντες οὖν καὶ ἀποβάντες ὡς ἂν ἐκ μακρᾶς ταλαιπωρίας πολὺν μὲν ἐπὶ τῆς γῆς χρόνον ἐκείμεθα. διαναστάντες δὲ ὅμως ἀπεκρίναμεν ἡμῶν αὐτῶν τριάκοντα μὲν φύλακας τῆς νεὼς παραμένειν, εἴ-
80 κοσι δὲ σὺν ἐμοὶ ἀνελθεῖν ἐπὶ κατασκοπῇ τῶν ἐν τῇ νήσῳ.

We explore the island, wherein are rivers of wine and other strange marvels.

Προελθόντες δὲ ὅσον σταδίους τρεῖς ἀπὸ τῆς θαλάττης δι᾽ ὕλης ὁρῶμέν τινα στήλην χαλκοῦ πεποιημένην, Ἑλληνικοῖς γράμμασι καταγεγραμμένην, ἀμυδροῖς δὲ καὶ
85 ἐκτετριμμένοις, λέγουσαν· "Ἄχρι τούτων Ἡρακλῆς καὶ Διόνυσος ἀφίκοντο." ἦν δὲ καὶ ἴχνη δύο πλησίον ἐπὶ πέτρας, τὸ μὲν πλεθμιαῖον τὸ δὲ ἔλαττον, ἐμοὶ δοκεῖν· τὸ μὲν τοῦ Διονύσου τὸ μικρότερον θάτερον δὲ Ἡρακλέους. προσκυνήσαντες δ᾽ οὖν προῄειμεν. οὔπω δὲ
90 πολὺ παρῄειμεν, καὶ ἐφιστάμεθα ποταμῷ οἶνον ῥέοντι, ὁμοιοτάτῳ μάλιστα οἷός περ ὁ Χῖός ἐστιν. ἄφθονον δὲ ἦν τὸ ῥεῦμα καὶ πολὺ, ὥστε ἐνιαχοῦ καὶ ναυσίπορον εἶναι δύνασθαι. ἐπῄει οὖν ἡμῖν πολὺ μᾶλλον πιστεύειν τῷ ἐπὶ τῆς στήλης ἐπιγράμματι, ὁρῶσι τὰ σημεῖα τῆς
95 Διονύσου ἐπιδημίας. δόξαν δέ μοι καὶ ὅθεν ἄρχεται ὁ ποταμὸς καταμαθεῖν, ἀνῄειν παρὰ τὸ ῥεῦμα· καὶ πηγὴν μὲν οὐδεμίαν εὗρον αὐτοῦ πολλὰς δὲ καὶ μεγάλας ἀμπέλους, πλήρεις βοτρύων· παρὰ δὲ τὴν ῥίζαν ἑκάστης ἀπέρρει σταγὼν οἴνου διαυγοῦς, ἀφ᾽ ὧν ἐγίγνετο ὁ ποτα-
100 μός. ἦν δὲ καὶ ἰχθῦς ἐν αὐτῷ πολλοὺς ἰδεῖν, οἴνῳ μά-

λιστα καὶ τὴν χροιὰν καὶ τὴν γεῦσιν προσεοικότας. ἡμεῖς γοῦν ἀγρεύσαντες αὐτῶν τινὰς καὶ ἐμφαγόντες ἐμεθύσθημεν· ἀμέλει καὶ ἀνατεμόντες αὐτοὺς εὑρίσκομεν τρυγὸς μεστούς. ὕστερον μέντοι ἐπινοήσαντες, τοὺς ἄλλους ἰχθῦς τοὺς ἀπὸ τοῦ ὕδατος παραμιγνύντες, ἐκεράννυμεν τὸ σφοδρὸν τῆς οἰνοφαγίας. τότε δὲ τὸν ποταμὸν διαπεράσαντες, ᾗ διαβατὸς ἦν, εὕρομεν ἀμπέλων χρῆμα τεράστιον· τὸ μὲν γὰρ ἀπὸ τῆς γῆς, ὁ στέλεχος αὐτὸς εὐερνὴς καὶ παχύς· τὸ δ' ἄνω γυναῖκες ἦσαν, ὅσον ἐκ τῶν λαγόνων, ἅπαντ' ἔχουσαι τέλεια. τοιαύτην παρ' ἡμῖν τὴν Δάφνην γράφουσιν ἄρτι τοῦ Ἀπόλλωνος καταλαμβάνοντος ἀποδενδρουμένην. ἀπὸ δὲ τῶν δακτύλων ἄκρων ἐξεφύοντο αὐταῖς οἱ κλάδοι, καὶ μεστοὶ ἦσαν βοτρύων. καὶ μὴν καὶ τὰς κεφαλὰς ἐκόμων ἕλιξί τε καὶ φύλλοις καὶ βότρυσι. προσελθόντας δὲ ἡμᾶς ἠσπάζοντό τε καὶ ἐδεξιοῦντο, αἱ μὲν Λύδιον αἱ δὲ Ἰνδικὴν αἱ πλεῖσται δὲ τὴν Ἑλλάδα φωνὴν προϊέμεναι. καὶ ἐφίλουν δὲ ἡμᾶς τοῖς στόμασιν· ὁ δὲ φιληθεὶς αὐτίκα ἐμέθυε καὶ παράφορος ἦν. δρέπεσθαι μέντοι οὐ παρεῖχον τοῦ καρποῦ, ἀλλὰ ἤλγουν καὶ ἐβόων ἀποσπωμένου. καταλιπόντες δ' αὐτοὺς ἐπὶ ναῦν ἐφεύγομεν, καὶ τοῖς ἀπολειφθεῖσι διηγούμεθα ἐλθόντες τὰ πάντα.

A whirlwind carries us through the air and deposits us in the Moon. We are introduced to its king, Endymion.

Καὶ δὴ λαβόντες ἀμφορέας τινὰς καὶ ὑδρευσάμενοί τε ἅμα καὶ ἐκ τοῦ ποταμοῦ οἰνισάμενοι, καὶ αὐτοῦ πλησίον ἐπὶ τῆς ἠϊόνος αὐλισάμενοι, ἕωθεν ἀνήχθημεν οὐ σφόδρα βιαίῳ πνεύματι. περὶ μεσημβρίαν δὲ, οὐκέτι τῆς νήσου φαινομένης, ἄφνω τυφὼν ἐπιγενόμενος καὶ περιδινήσας τὴν ναῦν, καὶ μετεωρίσας ὅσον ἐπὶ σταδίους

τρισχιλίους, οὐκέτι καθῆκεν εἰς τὸ πέλαγος, ἀλλ' ἄνω
130 μετέωρον ἐξηρτημένην ἄνεμος ἐμπεσὼν τοῖς ἱστίοις ἔφερε
κολπώσας τὴν ὀθόνην. ἑπτὰ δὲ ἡμέρας καὶ τὰς ἴσας
νύκτας ἀεροδρομήσαντες ὀγδόῃ καθορῶμεν γῆν τινα
μεγάλην ἐν τῷ ἀέρι, καθάπερ νῆσον, λαμπρὰν καὶ
σφαιροειδῆ καὶ φωτὶ μεγάλῳ καταλαμπομένην. προσ-
135 ενεχθέντες δ' αὐτῇ καὶ ὁρμισάμενοι ἀπέβημεν. ἐπι-
σκοποῦντες δὲ τὴν χώραν εὑρίσκομεν οἰκουμένην τε καὶ
γεωργουμένην· ἡμέρας μὲν οὖν οὐδὲν αὐτόθεν καθεω-
ρῶμεν· νυκτὸς δ' ἐπιγενομένης ἐφαίνοντο ἡμῖν καὶ ἄλλαι
νῆσοι πλησίον, αἱ μὲν μείζους αἱ δὲ μικρότεραι, πυρὶ
140 τὴν χρόαν προσεοικυῖαι· καὶ ἄλλη δέ τις γῆ κάτω, καὶ
πόλεις ἐν αὐτῇ καὶ ποταμοὺς ἔχουσα καὶ πελάγη καὶ
ὕλας καὶ ὄρη. ταύτην οὖν τὴν καθ' ἡμᾶς οἰκουμένην
εἰκάζομεν. δόξαν δὲ ἡμῖν καὶ ἔτι πορρωτέρω προελθεῖν,
ξυνελήφθημεν, τοῖς Ἱππογύποις παρ' αὐτοῖς καλουμένοις
145 ἀπαντήσαντες. οἱ δὲ Ἱππόγυποι οὗτοί εἰσιν ἄνδρες ἐπὶ
γυπῶν μεγάλων ὀχούμενοι, καὶ καθάπερ ἵπποις τοῖς
ὀρνέοις χρώμενοι· μεγάλοι γὰρ οἱ γῦπες καὶ ὡς ἐπίπαν
τρικέφαλοι. μάθοι δ' ἄν τις τὸ μέγεθος αὐτῶν ἐντεῦθεν·
νεὼς γὰρ μεγάλης φορτίδος ἱστοῦ ἕκαστον τῶν πτερῶν
150 μακρότερον καὶ παχύτερον φέρουσι. τούτοις οὖν τοῖς
Ἱππογύποις προστέτακται περιπετομένοις τὴν γῆν, εἴ
τις εὑρεθείη ξένος, ἄγειν ὡς τὸν βασιλέα· καὶ δὴ καὶ
ἡμᾶς ξυλλαβόντες ἄγουσιν ὡς αὐτόν. ὁ δὲ θεασάμενος
καὶ ἀπὸ τῆς στολῆς εἰκάσας, "Ἕλληνες ἆρα," ἔφη, "ὑμεῖς,
155 ὦ ξένοι;" συμφησάντων δὲ ἡμῶν, "πῶς οὖν ἀφίκεσθε,"
ἔφη, "τοσοῦτον ἀέρα διελθόντες;" καὶ ἡμεῖς τὸ πᾶν αὐτῷ
διηγούμεθα· καὶ ὃς ἀρξάμενος, τὸ καθ' ἑαυτὸν ἡμῖν
διεξῄει, ὡς καὶ αὐτὸς ἄνθρωπος ὢν, τοὔνομα Ἐνδυμίων,
ἀπὸ τῆς ἡμετέρας γῆς καθεύδων ἀναρπασθείη ποτέ,

καὶ ἀφικόμενος βασιλεύσειε τῆς χώρας. εἶναι δὲ τὴν 160
γῆν ἐκείνην ἔλεγε τὴν ἡμῖν κάτω φαινομένην Σελήνην.
ἀλλὰ θαρρεῖν τε παρεκελεύετο καὶ μηδένα κίνδυνον
ὑφορᾶσθαι· πάντα γὰρ ἡμῖν παρέσεσθαι, ὧν δεόμεθα.
"Ἢν δὲ καὶ κατορθώσω," ἔφη, "τὸν πόλεμον, ὃν ἐκφέρω
νῦν πρὸς τοὺς τὸν ἥλιον κατοικοῦντας, ἁπάντων εὐδαιμο- 165
νέστατα παρ' ἐμοὶ καταβιώσετε."

Impending battle between the inhabitants of the Moon and those of the Sun. The forces of Endymion and their equipment.

Καὶ ἡμεῖς ἠρόμεθα τίνες τε εἶεν οἱ πολέμιοι καὶ τὴν
αἰτίαν τῆς διαφορᾶς· ὁ δὲ, "Φαέθων," φησὶν, "ὁ τῶν ἐν τῷ
ἡλίῳ κατοικούντων βασιλεὺς, (οἰκεῖται γὰρ δὴ κἀκεῖνος,
ὥσπερ καὶ ἡ Σελήνη) πολὺν ἤδη πρὸς ἡμᾶς πολεμεῖ χρό- 170
νον. ἤρξατο δὲ ἐξ αἰτίας τοιαύτης· τῶν ἐν τῇ ἀρχῇ
τῇ ἐμῇ ποτε τοὺς ἀπορωτάτους συναγαγὼν ἐβουλήθην
ἀποικίαν ἐς τὸν Ἑωσφόρον στεῖλαι, ὄντα ἔρημον καὶ
ὑπὸ μηδενὸς κατοικούμενον· ὁ τοίνυν Φαέθων φθονήσας
ἐκώλυσε τὴν ἀποικίαν, κατὰ μέσον τὸν πόρον ἀπαντήσας 175
ἐπὶ τῶν Ἱππομυρμήκων. τότε μὲν οὖν νικηθέντες (οὐ
γὰρ ἦμεν ἀντίπαλοι τῇ παρασκευῇ) ἀνεχωρήσαμεν· νῦν
δὲ βούλομαι αὖθις ἐξενεγκεῖν τὸν πόλεμον, καὶ ἀποστεῖ-
λαι τὴν ἀποικίαν. ἢν οὖν ἐθέλητε, κοινωνήσατέ μοι
τοῦ στόλου· γῦπας δὲ ὑμῖν ἐγὼ παρέξω τῶν βασιλικῶν 180
ἕνα ἑκάστῳ καὶ τὴν ἄλλην ὅπλισιν. αὔριον δὲ ποιησό-
μεθα τὴν ἔξοδον." "Οὕτως," ἔφην ἐγὼ, "γιγνέσθω, ἐπειδή
σοι δοκεῖ." τότε μὲν οὖν παρ' αὐτῷ ἑστιαθέντες ἐμείνα-
μεν· ἕωθεν δὲ διαναστάντες ἐταττόμεθα· καὶ γὰρ οἱ
σκοποὶ πλησίον εἶναι ἐσήμαινον τοὺς πολεμίους. τὸ μὲν 185
οὖν πλῆθος τῆς στρατιᾶς δέκα μυριάδες ἐγένοντο, ἄνευ

τῶν σκευοφόρων καὶ τῶν μηχανοποιῶν καὶ τῶν πεζῶν καὶ τῶν ξένων συμμάχων. τούτων δὲ ὀκτακισμύριοι μὲν ἦσαν οἱ Ἱππόγυποι, δισμύριοι δὲ οἱ ἐπὶ τῶν λαχαν-
190 οπτέρων. ὄρνεον δὲ καὶ τοῦτό ἐστι μέγιστον, ἀντὶ τῶν πτερῶν λαχάνοις πάντη λάσιον· τὰ δ' ὠκύπτερα ἔχει θριδακίνοις φύλλοις μάλιστα προσεοικότα. ἐπὶ δὲ τούτοις οἱ Κεγχροβόλοι ἐτετάχατο καὶ οἱ Σκοροδομάχοι. ἦλθον δὲ καὶ ἀπὸ τῆς Ἄρκτου σύμμαχοι, τρισμύριοι
195 μὲν Ψυλλοτοξόται πεντακισμύριοι δὲ Ἀνεμοδρόμοι. τούτων δὲ οἱ μὲν Ψυλλοτοξόται ἐπὶ ψυλλῶν μεγάλων ἱππάζονται, ὅθεν καὶ τὴν προσηγορίαν ἔχουσι· μέγεθος δὲ τῶν ψυλλῶν ὅσον δώδεκα ἐλέφαντες. οἱ δ' Ἀνεμοδρόμοι πεζοὶ μέν εἰσι φέρονται δ' ἐν τῷ ἀέρι ἄνευ πτε-
200 ρῶν. ὁ δὲ τρόπος τῆς φορᾶς τοιόσδε· χιτῶνας ποδήρεις ὑπεζωσμένοι, κολπώσαντες αὐτοὺς τῷ ἀνέμῳ καθάπερ ἱστία, φέρονται ὥσπερ τὰ σκάφη· τὰ πολλὰ δ' οἱ τοιοῦτοι ἐν ταῖς μάχαις πελτασταί εἰσιν. ἐλέγοντο δὲ καὶ ἀπὸ τῶν ὑπὲρ τὴν Καππαδοκίαν ἀστέρων ἥξειν
205 Στρουθοβάλανοι μὲν ἑπτακισμύριοι Ἱππογέρανοι δὲ πεντακισχίλιοι. τούτους ἐγὼ οὐκ ἐθεασάμην· οὐ γὰρ ἀφίκοντο· διόπερ οὐδὲ γράψαι αὐτῶν τὰς φύσεις ἐτόλμησα· τεράστια γὰρ καὶ ἄπιστα περὶ αὐτῶν ἐλέγετο. αὕτη μὲν τοῦ Ἐνδυμίωνος ἡ δύναμις. σκευὴ δὲ πάν-
210 των ἡ αὐτή· κράνη μὲν ἀπὸ τῶν κυάμων (μεγάλοι γὰρ παρ' αὐτοῖς οἱ κύαμοι καὶ καρτεροί) θώρακες δὲ φολιδωτοὶ πάντες θέρμινοι· τὰ γὰρ λέπη τῶν θέρμων συρράπτοντες ποιοῦνται θώρακας· ἄρρηκτον δ' ἐκεῖ γίγνεται τοῦ θέρμου τὸ λέπος, ὥσπερ κέρας· ἀσπίδες δὲ καὶ
215 ξίφη, οἷα τὰ Ἑλληνικά.

Both armies are drawn up for battle. Description of the forces of Phaethon, the king of the Sun.

Ἐπεὶ δὲ καιρὸς ἦν, ἐτάξαντο ὧδε· τὸ μὲν δεξιὸν κέρας
εἶχον οἱ Ἱππόγυποι καὶ ὁ βασιλεὺς τοὺς ἀρίστους περὶ
αὑτὸν ἔχων· καὶ ἡμεῖς ἐν τούτοις ἦμεν· τὸ δ' εὐώνυμον οἱ
Λαχανόπτεροι· τὸ δὲ μέσον οἱ σύμμαχοι ὡς ἕκαστοι· τὸ
δὲ πεζὸν ἦσαν μὲν ἀμφὶ τὰς ἑξακισχιλίας μυριάδας· 220
ἐτάχθησαν δὲ οὕτως. ἀράχναι παρ' αὐτοῖς πολλοὶ καὶ
μεγάλοι γίγνονται, πολὺ τῶν Κυκλάδων νήσων ἕκαστος
μείζων. τούτοις προσέταξε διυφῆναι τὸν μεταξὺ τῆς
Σελήνης καὶ τοῦ Ἑωσφόρου ἀέρα. ὡς δὲ τάχιστα
ἐξειργάσαντο καὶ πεδίον ἐποίησαν, ἐπὶ τούτου παρέταξε 225
τὸ πεζόν. ἡγεῖτο δὲ αὐτῶν Νυκτερίων ὁ Εὐδιάνακτος
τρίτος αὐτός. τῶν δὲ πολεμίων τὸ μὲν εὐώνυμον εἶχον
οἱ Ἱππομύρμηκες καὶ ἐν αὐτοῖς ὁ Φαέθων· θηρία δέ ἐστι
μέγιστα ὑπόπτερα, τοῖς παρ' ἡμῖν μύρμηξι προσεικότα,
πλὴν τοῦ μεγέθους· ὁ γὰρ μέγιστος αὐτῶν καὶ δίπλεθρος 230
ἦν. ἐμάχοντο δὲ οὐ μόνον οἱ ἐπ' αὐτῶν ἀλλὰ καὶ αὐτοὶ
μάλιστα τοῖς κέρασιν· ἐλέγοντο δὲ οὗτοι εἶναι ἀμφὶ τὰς
πέντε μυριάδας. ἐπὶ δὲ τοῦ δεξιοῦ αὐτῶν ἐτάχθησαν
οἱ Ἀεροκώνωπες, ὄντες καὶ οὗτοι ἀμφὶ τὰς πέντε μυριάδας, πάντες τοξόται, κώνωψι μεγάλοις ἐποχούμενοι· 235
μετὰ δὲ τούτους οἱ Ἀεροκόρακες, ψιλοί τε ὄντες καὶ πε-
ζοί, πλὴν μάχιμοί γε καὶ οὗτοι· πόρρωθεν γὰρ ἐσφεν-
δόνων ῥαφανίδας ὑπερμεγέθεις· καὶ ὁ βληθεὶς οὐδ' ἐπ'
ὀλίγον ἀντέχειν ἠδύνατο· ἀπέθνησκε δὲ, δυσωδίας τινὸς
αὐτίκα τῷ τραύματι ἐγγιγνομένης· ἐλέγοντο δὲ χρίειν τὰ 240
βέλη μαλάχης ἰῷ. ἐχόμενοι δ' αὐτῶν ἐτάχθησαν οἱ
Καυλομύκητες, ὁπλῖται ὄντες καὶ ἀγχέμαχοι, τὸ πλῆθος
μυριοι ἐκλήθησαν δὲ Καυλομύκητες, ὅτι ἀσπίσι μὲν

μυκητίναις ἐχρῶντο δόρασι δὲ καυλίνοις, τοῖς ἀπὸ τῶν
245 ἀσπαράγων. πλησίον δὲ αὐτῶν οἱ Κυνοβάλανοι ἔστησαν, οὓς ἔπεμψαν αὐτῷ οἱ τὸν Σείριον κατοικοῦντες, πεντακισχίλιοι, καὶ οὗτοι ἄνδρες κυνοπρόσωποι ἐπὶ βαλάνων πτερωτῶν μαχόμενοι. ἐλέγοντο δὲ κἀκείνων ὑστερίζειν τῶν συμμάχων, οὕς τε ἀπὸ τοῦ Γαλαξίου
250 μετεπέμπετο σφενδονήτας, καὶ οἱ Νεφελοκένταυροι. ἀλλ' ἐκεῖνοι μὲν, τῆς μάχης ἤδη κεκριμένης, ἀφίκοντο, ὡς μήποτε ὤφελον· οἱ σφενδονῆται δὲ οὐδὲ ὅλως παρεγένοντο· διόπερ φασὶν αὐτοῖς ὕστερον ὀργισθέντα τὸν Φαέθοντα πυρπολῆσαι τὴν χώραν. τοιαύτῃ μὲν καὶ Φαέθων
255 ἐπῄει παρασκευῇ.

*The fight begins, **in which** the Moon's army is at first victorious. The arrival of the Cloud-centaurs reverses our good fortune.*

Συμμίξαντες δὲ, ἐπειδὴ τὰ σημεῖα ἤρθη καὶ ὠγκήσαντο ἑκατέρων οἱ ὄνοι (τούτοις γὰρ ἀντὶ σαλπιστῶν χρῶνται), ἐμάχοντο. καὶ τὸ μὲν εὐώνυμον τῶν Ἡλιωτῶν αὐτίκα ἔφυγεν οὐδ' ἐς χεῖρας δεξάμενον τοὺς Ἱππογύπους, καὶ
260 ἡμεῖς εἰπόμεθα κτείνοντες· τὸ δεξιὸν δ' αὐτῶν ἐκράτει τοῦ ἐπὶ τῷ ἡμετέρῳ εὐωνύμου· καὶ ἐπεξῆλθον οἱ Ἀεροκώνωπες διώκοντες ἄχρι πρὸς τοὺς πεζούς. ἐνταῦθα δὲ κἀκείνων ἐπιβοηθούντων ἔφυγον ἐπικλίναντες, καὶ μάλιστα ἐπεὶ ᾔσθοντο τοὺς ἐπὶ τῷ εὐωνύμῳ σφῶν νενικη-
265 μένους. τῆς δὲ τροπῆς λαμπρᾶς γενομένης, πολλοὶ μὲν ζῶντες ἡλίσκοντο πολλοὶ δὲ καὶ ἀνῃροῦντο, καὶ τὸ αἷμα ἔρρει πολὺ μὲν ἐπὶ τῶν νεφῶν, ὥστε αὐτὰ βάπτεσθαι καὶ ἐρυθρὰ φαίνεσθαι, οἷα παρ' ἡμῖν δυομένου τοῦ ἡλίου φαίνεται· πολὺ δὲ καὶ εἰς τὴν γῆν κατέσταζεν, ὥστε με
270 εἰκάζειν, μὴ ἄρα τοιούτου τινὸς καὶ πάλαι ἄνω γενομένου

Ὅμηρος ὑπέλαβεν αἵματι ὗσαι τὸν Δία ἐπὶ τῷ τοῦ Σαρπηδόνος θανάτῳ. ἀναστρέψαντες δὲ ἀπὸ τῆς διώξεως δύο τρόπαια ἐστήσαμεν, τὸ μὲν ἐπὶ τῶν ἀραχνίων τῆς πεζομαχίας τὸ δὲ τῆς ἀερομαχίας ἐπὶ τῶν νεφῶν. ἄρτι δὲ τούτων γιγνομένων ἠγγέλλοντο ὑπὸ τῶν σκοπῶν 275 οἱ Νεφελοκένταυροι προσελαύνοντες, οὓς ἔδει πρὸ τῆς μάχης ἐλθεῖν τῷ Φαέθοντι. καὶ δὴ ἐφαίνοντο προσιόντες, θέαμα παραδοξότατον, ἐξ ἵππων πτερωτῶν καὶ ἀνθρώπων συγκείμενοι· μέγεθος δὲ, τῶν μὲν ἀνθρώπων ὅσον τοῦ Ῥοδίου Κολοσσοῦ ἐξ ἡμισείας ἐς τὸ ἄνω· τῶν δ' 280 ἵππων ὅσον νεὼς μεγάλης φορτίδος. τὸ μέντοι πλῆθος αὐτῶν οὐκ ἀνέγραψα, μή τῳ καὶ ἄπιστον δόξῃ, τοσοῦτον ἦν. ἡγεῖτο δὲ αὐτῶν ὁ ἐκ τοῦ Ζωδιακοῦ τοξότης. ἐπεὶ δὲ ᾔσθοντο τοὺς φίλους νενικημένους, ἐπὶ μὲν τὸν Φαέθοντα ἔπεμπον ἀγγελίαν αὖθις ἐπιέναι· αὐτοὶ δὲ 285 διαταξάμενοι τεταραγμένοις ἐμπίπτουσι τοῖς Σεληνίταις, ἀτάκτοις περὶ τὴν δίωξιν καὶ τὰ λάφυρα διεσκεδασμένοις· καὶ πάντας μὲν τρέπουσιν, αὐτὸν δὲ τὸν βασιλέα καταδιώκουσι πρὸς τὴν πόλιν καὶ τὰ πλεῖστα τῶν ὀρνέων αὐτοῦ κτείνουσιν· ἀνέσπασαν δὲ καὶ τὰ τρόπαια, 290 καὶ κατέδραμον ἅπαν τὸ ὑπὸ τῶν ἀραχνῶν πεδίον ὑφασμένον, ἐμὲ δὲ καὶ δύο τινὰς τῶν ἑταίρων ἐζώγρησαν. ἤδη δὲ παρῆν καὶ ὁ Φαέθων καὶ αὖθις ἄλλα τρόπαια ὑπ' ἐκείνων ἵστατο.

We are taken captive into the Sun. A wall of clouds is built to intercept the light. Terms of peace. Being released and sent back to the Moon, we are pressed to stay, but decline.

Ἡμεῖς μὲν οὖν ἀπηγόμεθα ἐς τὸν Ἥλιον αὐθημερὸν, 295 τὼ χεῖρε ὀπίσω δεθέντες ἀραχνίου ἀποκόμματι. οἱ δὲ πολιορκεῖν μὲν οὐκ ἔγνωσαν τὴν πόλιν· ἀναστρέψαντες

δὲ τὸ μεταξὺ τοῦ ἀέρος ἀπετείχιζον, ὥστε μηκέτι τας αὐγὰς ἀπὸ τοῦ ἡλίου πρὸς τὴν σελήνην διήκειν. τὸ δὲ
300 τεῖχος ἦν διπλοῦν, νεφελωτόν· ὥστε σαφὴς ἔκλειψις τῆς Σελήνης ἐγεγόνει καὶ νυκτὶ διηνεκεῖ πᾶσα κατείχετο. πιεζόμενος δὲ τούτοις ὁ Ἐνδυμίων πέμψας ἱκέτευε καθαιρεῖν τὸ οἰκοδόμημα, καὶ μὴ σφᾶς περιορᾶν ἐν σκότῳ βιοτεύοντας· ὑπισχνεῖτο δὲ καὶ φόρους τελέσειν καὶ
305 σύμμαχος ἔσεσθαι καὶ μηκέτι πολεμήσειν· καὶ ὁμήρους ἐπὶ τούτοις δοῦναι ἤθελεν. οἱ δὲ περὶ τὸν Φαέθοντα, γενομένης δὶς ἐκκλησίας, τῇ προτεραίᾳ μὲν οὐδὲν παρέλυσαν τῆς ὀργῆς τῇ ὑστεραίᾳ δὲ μετέγνωσαν. καὶ ἐγένετο ἡ εἰρήνη ἐπὶ τούτοις. "Κατὰ τάδε συνθήκας
310 ἐποιήσαντο οἱ Ἡλιῶται καὶ οἱ σύμμαχοι πρὸς Σεληνίτας καὶ τοὺς συμμάχους, ἐπὶ τῷ καταλῦσαι μὲν τοὺς Ἡλιώτας τὸ διατείχισμα καὶ μηκέτι ἐς τὴν Σελήνην ἐσβάλλειν, ἀποδοῦναι δὲ καὶ τοὺς αἰχμαλώτους, ῥητῶν ἕκαστον χρημάτων· τοὺς δὲ Σεληνίτας ἀφεῖναι μὲν αὐτονόμους
315 τούς γε ἄλλους ἀστέρας, ὅπλα δὲ μὴ ἐπιφέρειν τοῖς Ἡλιώταις, συμμαχεῖν δὲ τῇ ἀλλήλων, ἤν τις ἐπίῃ· φόρον δὲ ὑποτελεῖν ἑκάστου ἔτους τὸν βασιλέα τῶν Σεληνιτῶν τῷ βασιλεῖ τῶν Ἡλιωτῶν δρόσου ἀμφορέας μυρίους· καὶ ὁμήρους δὲ σφῶν αὐτῶν δοῦναι μυ-
320 ρίους, τὴν δ' ἀποικίαν τὴν ἐς τὸν Ἑωσφόρον κοινὴν ποιεῖσθαι, καὶ μετέχειν τῶν ἄλλων τὸν βουλόμενον. ἐγγράψαι δὲ τὰς συνθήκας στήλῃ ἠλεκτρίνῃ καὶ ἀναστῆσαι ἐν μέσῳ τῷ ἀέρι ἐπὶ τοῖς μεθορίοις. ὤμοσαν δὲ Ἡλιωτῶν μὲν Πυρωνίδης καὶ Θερίτης καὶ Φλόγιος· Σεληνιτῶν
325 δὲ Νύκτωρ καὶ Μήνιος καὶ Πολυλαμπής." τοιαύτη μὲν ἡ εἰρήνη ἐγένετο· εὐθὺς δὲ τὸ τεῖχος καθῃρεῖτο καὶ ἡμᾶς τοὺς αἰχμαλώτους ἀπέδοσαν. ἐπεὶ δὲ ἀφικόμεθα ἐς τὴν Σελήνην, ὑπηντίαζον ἡμᾶς καὶ ἠσπάζοντο

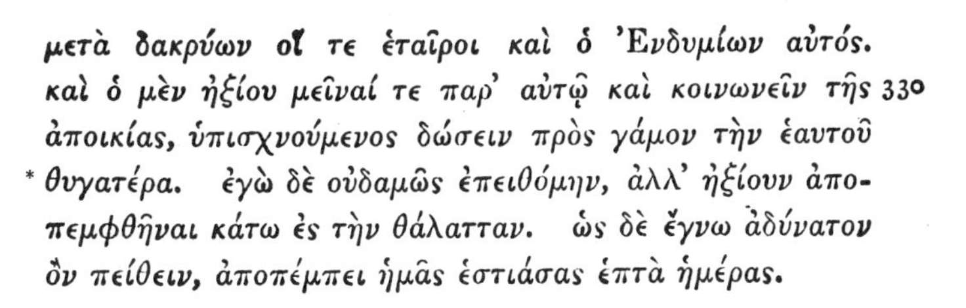

μετὰ δακρύων οἵ τε ἑταῖροι καὶ ὁ Ἐνδυμίων αὐτός. καὶ ὁ μὲν ἠξίου μεῖναί τε παρ' αὐτῷ καὶ κοινωνεῖν τῆς 330 ἀποικίας, ὑπισχνούμενος δώσειν πρὸς γάμον τὴν ἑαυτοῦ * θυγατέρα. ἐγὼ δὲ οὐδαμῶς ἐπειθόμην, ἀλλ' ἠξίουν ἀποπεμφθῆναι κάτω ἐς τὴν θάλατταν. ὡς δὲ ἔγνω ἀδύνατον ὂν πείθειν, ἀποπέμπει ἡμᾶς ἑστιάσας ἑπτὰ ἡμέρας.

Manners and customs in the Moon. The food and drink and bodily structure of its inhabitants.

*Ἃ δ' ἐν τῷ μεταξὺ διατρίβων ἐν τῇ Σελήνῃ κατενόησα 335 καινὰ καὶ παράδοξα, ταῦτα βούλομαι εἰπεῖν. τροφὴ μὲν πᾶσιν ἡ αὐτή· ἐπειδὰν γὰρ πῦρ ἀνακαύσωσι, βατράχους ὀπτῶσιν ἐπὶ τῶν ἀνθράκων· πολλοὶ δὲ παρ' αὐτοῖς εἰσιν ἐν τῷ ἀέρι πετόμενοι· ὀπτωμένων δὲ, περικαθεζόμενοι, ὥσπερ δὴ περὶ τράπεζαν, λάπτουσι τὸν ἀναθυμιώμενον 340 καπνὸν καὶ εὐωχοῦνται. σίτῳ μὲν δὴ τρέφονται τοιούτῳ· ποτὸν δὲ αὐτοῖς ἐστιν ἀὴρ ἀποθλιβόμενος ἐς κύλικα, καὶ ὑγρὸν ἀνιεὶς, ὥσπερ δρόσον. καλὸς δὲ νομίζεται παρ' αὐτοῖς, ἤν πού τις φαλακρὸς καὶ ἄκομος ᾖ· τοὺς δὲ κομήτας καὶ μυσάττονται. ἐπὶ δὲ τῶν κομητῶν ἀστέρων 345 τοὐναντίον τοὺς κομήτας καλοὺς νομίζουσιν· ἐπεδήμουν γάρ τινες, οἳ καὶ περὶ ἐκείνων διηγοῦντο. καὶ μὴν καὶ γένεια φύουσι μικρὸν ὑπὲρ τὰ γόνατα. καὶ ὄνυχας ἐν τοῖς ποσὶν οὐκ ἔχουσιν, ἀλλὰ πάντες εἰσὶ μονοδάκτυλοι. ἀπομύττονται δὲ μέλι δριμύτατον· κἀπειδὰν ἢ πονῶσιν 350 ἢ γυμνάζωνται, γάλακτι πᾶν τὸ σῶμα ἱδροῦσιν, ὥστε καὶ τυροὺς ἀπ' αὐτοῦ πήγνυσθαι, ὀλίγον τοῦ μέλιτος ἐπιστάξαντες· ἔλαιον δὲ ποιοῦνται ἀπὸ τῶν κρομμύων πάνυ λιπαρόν τε καὶ εὐῶδες, ὥσπερ μύρον. ἀμπέλους δὲ πολλὰς ἔχουσιν ὑδροφόρους· αἱ γὰρ ῥᾶγες τῶν βοτρύων 355 εἰσὶν ὥσπερ χάλαζα. καί μοι δοκεῖ, ἐπειδὰν ἐμπεσὼν

*See addendum, pp. 78-79.

ἄνεμος διασείσῃ τὰς ἀμπέλους ἐκείνας, τότε πρὸς ἡμᾶς καταπίπτει ἡ χάλαζα, διαρραγέντων τῶν βοτρύων. τῇ μέντοι γαστρὶ ὥσπερ πήρᾳ χρῶνται, τιθέντες ἐν αὐτῇ
360 ὅσων δέονται. ἀνοικτὴ γὰρ αὐτοῖς αὕτη καὶ πάλιν κλειστή ἐστιν· ἔντερον δὲ ἐν αὐτῇ οὐδὲ ἧπαρ φαίνεται, ἢ τοῦτο μόνον, ὅτι δασεῖα ἔντοσθε καὶ λάσιός ἐστιν, ὥστε καὶ τὰ νεογνὰ, ἐπειδὰν ῥιγῶσιν, ἐς ταύτην ὑποδύεται. ἐσθὴς δὲ τοῖς μὲν πλουσίοις ὑαλίνη, μαλθακή· τοῖς
365 πένησι δὲ χαλκῆ ὑφαντή· πολύχαλκα γὰρ τὰ ἐκεῖ χωρία, καὶ ἐργάζονται τὸν χαλκὸν ὕδατι ὑποβρέξαντες, ὥσπερ τὰ ἔρια. περὶ μέντοι τῶν ὀφθαλμῶν, οἵους ἔχουσιν, ὀκνῶ μὲν εἰπεῖν, μή τίς με νομίσῃ ψεύδεσθαι διὰ τὸ ἄπιστον τοῦ λόγου· ὅμως δὲ καὶ τοῦτο ἐρῶ. τοὺς ὀφθαλμοὺς
370 περιαιρετοὺς ἔχουσι· καὶ ὁ βουλόμενος ἐξελὼν τοὺς αὑτοῦ φυλάττει, ἔστ' ἂν δεηθῇ ἰδεῖν· οὕτω δὲ ἐνθέμενος ὁρᾷ. καὶ πολλοὶ τοὺς σφετέρους ἀπολέσαντες παρ' ἄλλων χρησάμενοι ὁρῶσιν. εἰσὶ δ' οἳ καὶ πολλοὺς ἀποθέτους ἔχουσιν, οἱ πλούσιοι. τὰ ὦτα δὲ πλατάνων
375 φύλλα ἐστὶν αὐτοῖς· εἰσὶ δ' οἳ καὶ ξύλινα ἔχουσιν. ἐπειδὰν δὲ γηράσῃ ὁ ἄνθρωπος, οὐκ ἀποθνήσκει, ἀλλ' ὥσπερ ὁ καπνὸς διαλυόμενος ἀὴρ γίγνεται. καὶ μὴν καὶ ἄλλο θαῦμα ἐν τοῖς βασιλείοις ἐθεασάμην. κάτοπτρον μέγιστον κεῖται ὑπὲρ φρέατος οὐ πάνυ βαθέος. ἂν μὲν οὖν
380 εἰς τὸ φρέαρ καταβῇ τις, ἀκούει πάντων τῶν παρ' ἡμῖν ἐν τῇ γῇ λεγομένων· ἐὰν δὲ εἰς τὸ κάτοπτρον ἀποβλέψῃ, πάσας μὲν πόλεις πάντα δὲ ἔθνη ὁρᾷ, ὥσπερ ἐφεστὼς ἑκάστοις· τότε καὶ τοὺς οἰκείους ἐγὼ ἐθεασάμην καὶ πᾶσαν τὴν πατρίδα· εἰ δὲ κἀκεῖνοί με ἑώρων
385 οὐκ ἔχω τὸ ἀσφαλὲς εἰπεῖν. ὅστις δὲ μὴ πιστεύει ταῦτα οὕτως ἔχειν, ἄν ποτε καὶ αὐτὸς ἐκεῖσε ἀφίκηται, εἴσεται ὡς ἀληθῆ λέγω.

Leaving the Moon, we are carried through the Zodiac to the City of Lanterns, and thence to Cloud-cuckoo-town.

Τότε δ' οὖν ἀσπασάμενοι τὸν βασιλέα καὶ τοὺς ἀμφ' αὐτὸν, ἐμβάντες ἀνήχθημεν, ἐμοὶ δὲ καὶ δῶρα ἔδωκεν ὁ Ἐνδυμίων δύο μὲν τῶν ὑαλίνων χιτώνων πέντε δὲ 390 χαλκοῦς καὶ πανοπλίαν θερμίνην· ἃ πάντα ἐν τῷ κήτει κατέλιπον. συνέπεμπε δὲ ἡμῖν καὶ Ἱππογύπους χιλίους, παραπέμψοντας ἄχρι σταδίων πεντακοσίων. ἐν δὲ τῷ παράπλῳ πολλὰς μὲν καὶ ἄλλας χώρας παρημείψαμεν προσέσχομεν δὲ καὶ τῷ Ἑωσφόρῳ ἄρτι συνοικιζομένῳ, 395 καὶ ἀποβάντες ὑδρευσάμεθα. ἐμβάντες δὲ εἰς τὸν Ζωδιακὸν ἐν ἀριστερᾷ παρήειμεν τὸν ἥλιον, ἐν χρῷ τὴν γῆν παραπλέοντες· οὐ γὰρ ἀπέβημεν, καίτοι πολλὰ τῶν ἑταίρων ἐπιθυμούντων· ἀλλ' ὁ ἄνεμος οὐκ ἐφῆκεν. ἐθεώμεθα μέντοι τὴν χώραν εὐθαλῆ τε καὶ πίονα καὶ 400 εὔυδρον καὶ πολλῶν ἀγαθῶν μεστήν. ἰδόντες δὲ ἡμᾶς οἱ Νεφελοκένταυροι, μισθοφοροῦντες παρὰ τῷ Φαέθοντι, ἐπέπτησαν ἐπὶ τὴν ναῦν, καὶ μαθόντες ἐνσπόνδους ἀνεχώρησαν. ἤδη δὲ καὶ οἱ Ἱππόγυποι ἀπεληλύθεσαν· πλεύσαντες δὲ τὴν ἐπιοῦσαν νύκτα καὶ ἡμέραν περὶ 405 ἑσπέραν ἀφικόμεθα ἐς τὴν Λυχνόπολιν καλουμένην, ἤδη τὸν κάτω πλοῦν διώκοντες· ἡ δὲ πόλις αὕτη κεῖται μεταξὺ τοῦ Πλειάδων καὶ τοῦ Ὑάδων ἀέρος, ταπεινοτέρα μέντοι πολὺ τοῦ Ζωδιακοῦ. ἀποβάντες δὲ ἄνθρωπον μὲν οὐδένα εὕρομεν λύχνους δὲ πολλοὺς περι- 410 θέοντας, καὶ ἐν τῇ ἀγορᾷ καὶ περὶ τὸν λιμένα διατρίβοντας, τοὺς μὲν μικροὺς καὶ ὥσπερ εἰπεῖν πένητας· ὀλίγους δὲ, τῶν μεγάλων καὶ δυνατῶν, πάνυ λαμπροὺς καὶ περιφανεῖς. οἰκήσεις δ' αὐτοῖς καὶ λυχνεῶνες ἰδίᾳ ἑκάστῳ ἐπεποίηντο, καὶ αὐτοὶ ὀνόματα εἶχον, ὥσπερ οἱ ἄνθρωποι, καὶ φωνὴν 415

προϊεμένων ἠκούομεν· καὶ οὐδὲν ἡμᾶς ἠδίκουν, ἀλλὰ και ἐπὶ ξενίᾳ ἐκάλουν· ἡμεῖς δὲ ὅμως ἐφοβούμεθα· καὶ οὔτε δειπνῆσαι οὔτε ὑπνῶσαί τις ἡμῶν ἐτόλμησεν. ἀρχεῖα δ' αὐτοῖς ἐν μέσῃ τῇ πόλει πεποίηται, ἔνθα ὁ ἄρχων
420 αὐτῶν δι' ὅλης νυκτὸς κάθηται, ὀνομαστὶ καλῶν ἕκαστον. ὃς δ' ἂν μὴ ὑπακούσῃ καταδικάζεται ἀποθανεῖν, ὡς λιπὼν τὴν τάξιν· ὁ δὲ θάνατός ἐστι σβεσθῆναι. παρεστῶτες δὲ καὶ ἡμεῖς ἑωρῶμεν τὰ γιγνόμενα, καὶ ἠκούομεν ἅμα τῶν λύχνων ἀπολογουμένων καὶ τὰς αἰτίας λεγόντων,
425 δι' ἃς ἐβράδυνον. ἔνθα καὶ τὸν ἡμέτερον λύχνον ἐγνώρισα, καὶ προσειπὼν αὐτὸν περὶ τῶν κατ' οἶκον ἐπυνθανόμην ὅπως ἔχοιεν· ὁ δέ μοι πάντα διηγήσατο. τὴν μὲν οὖν νύκτα ἐκείνην αὐτοῦ ἐμείναμεν· τῇ δὲ ἐπιούσῃ ἄραντες ἐπλέομεν ἤδη πλησίον τῶν νεφῶν. ἔνθα δὴ καὶ τὴν
430 Νεφελοκοκκυγίαν πόλιν ἰδόντες ἐθαυμάσαμεν, οὐ μέντοι ἐπέβημεν αὐτῆς· οὐ γὰρ εἴα τὸ πνεῦμα. βασιλεύειν μέντοι αὐτῶν ἐλέγετο Κορωνὸς ὁ Κοττυφίωνος. καὶ ἐγὼ ἐμνήσθην Ἀριστοφάνους τοῦ ποιητοῦ, ἀνδρὸς σοφοῦ καὶ ἀληθοῦς καὶ μάτην ἐφ' οἷς ἔγραψεν ἀπιστουμένου.

We descend to the Ocean again, and are swallowed, ship and all, by an enormous sea-monster.

435 Τρίτῃ δ' ἀπὸ ταύτης ἡμέρᾳ, καὶ τὸν Ὠκεανὸν ἤδη σαφῶς ἑωρῶμεν· γῆν δὲ οὐδαμοῦ, πλήν γε τῶν ἐν τῷ ἀέρι· καὶ αὗται δὲ πυροειδεῖς ἤδη καὶ ὑπεραυγεῖς ἐφαντάζοντο. τῇ τετάρτῃ δὲ περὶ μεσημβρίαν, μαλακῶς ἐνδιδόντος τοῦ πνεύματος καὶ συνιζάνοντος, ἐπὶ τὴν
440 θάλατταν κατετέθημεν. ὡς δὲ τοῦ ὕδατος ἐψαύσαμεν, θαυμάσιον ὡς ὑπερηδόμεθα καὶ ὑπερεχαίρομεν καὶ πᾶσαν εὐφροσύνην ἐκ τῶν παρόντων ἐποιούμεθα καὶ ἀποβάντες ἐνηχόμεθα· καὶ γὰρ ἔτυχε γαλήνη οὖσα καὶ εὐσταθοῦν

τὸ πέλαγος. ἔοικε δὲ ἀρχὴ κακῶν μειζόνων γίγνεσθαι πολλάκις ἡ πρὸς τὸ βέλτιον μεταβολή· καὶ γὰρ ἡμεῖς 445 δύο μόνας ἡμέρας ἐν εὐδίᾳ πλεύσαντες, τῆς τρίτης ὑποφαινούσης, πρὸς ἀνίσχοντα τὸν ἥλιον ἄφνω ὁρῶμεν θηρία καὶ κήτη, πολλὰ μὲν καὶ ἄλλα ἓν δὲ μέγιστον ἁπάντων, ὅσον σταδίων χιλίων καὶ πεντακοσίων τὸ μέγεθος· ἐπῄει δὲ κεχηνὸς καὶ πρὸ πολλοῦ ταράττον 450 τὴν θάλατταν ἀφρῷ τε περικλυζόμενον καὶ τοὺς ὀδόντας ἐκφαῖνον, ὀξεῖς πάντας ὥσπερ σκόλοπας καὶ λευκοὺς ὥσπερ ἐλεφαντίνους. ἡμεῖς μὲν οὖν τὸ ὕστατον ἀλλήλους προσειπόντες καὶ περιβάλλοντες ἐμένομεν· τὸ δὲ ἤδη παρῆν, καὶ ἀναρροφῆσαν ἡμᾶς αὐτῇ νηῒ κατέπιεν. οὐ 455 μέντοι ἔφθη συναράξαι τοῖς ὀδοῦσιν, ἀλλὰ διὰ τῶν ἀραιωμάτων ἡ ναῦς εἰς τὸ εἴσω διεξέπεσεν.

Description of the monster's inside, and what we found there.

Ἐπεὶ δὲ ἔνδον ἦμεν, τὸ μὲν πρῶτον σκότος ἦν, καὶ οὐδὲν ἑωρῶμεν· ὕστερον δὲ αὐτοῦ ἀναχανόντος εἴδομεν κύτος μέγα, καὶ πάντῃ πλατὺ καὶ ὑψηλὸν, ἱκανὸν 460 μυριάνδρῳ πόλει ἐνοικεῖν. ἔκειντο δ' ἐν μέσῳ καὶ μικροὶ ἰχθύες καὶ ἄλλα θηρία πολλὰ συγκεκομμένα καὶ πλοίων ἱστία καὶ ἄγκυραι καὶ ἀνθρώπων ὀστέα καὶ φορτία· κατὰ μέσον δὲ καὶ γῆ καὶ λόφοι ἦσαν, ἐμοὶ δοκεῖν, ἐκ τῆς ἰλύος ἣν κατέπινε συνιζάνουσα. ὕλη γοῦν ἐπ' αὐτῆς 465 καὶ δένδρα παντοῖα ἐπεφύκει, καὶ λάχανα ἐβεβλαστήκει, καὶ ἐῴκει πάντα ἐξειργασμένοις· περίμετρος δὲ τῆς γῆς στάδιοι διακόσιοι καὶ τετταράκοντα. ἦν δὲ ἰδεῖν καὶ ὄρνεα τὰ θαλάττια, λάρους καὶ ἀλκυόνας, ἐπὶ τῶν δένδρων νεοττεύοντα. τότε μὲν οὖν ἐπὶ πολὺ ἐδακρύομεν· ὕστερον 470 δὲ ἀναστήσας τοὺς ἑταίρους τὴν μὲν ναῦν ὑπεστηρίξαμεν·

αὐτοὶ δὲ τὰ πυρεῖα συντρίψαντες καὶ ἀνακαύσαντες δεῖπνον ἐκ τῶν παρόντων ἐποιούμεθα. παρέκειτο δὲ ἄφθονα καὶ παντοδαπὰ κρέα τῶν ἰχθύων, καὶ ὕδωρ ἔτι τὸ
475 ἐκ τοῦ Ἑωσφόρου εἴχομεν. τῇ ἐπιούσῃ δὲ διαναστάντες, εἴ ποτε ἀναχάνοι τὸ κῆτος, ἄλλοτε μὲν γῆν καὶ ὄρη ἑωρῶμεν ἄλλοτε δὲ μόνον τὸν οὐρανὸν, πολλάκις δὲ καὶ νήσους. καὶ γὰρ ᾐσθανόμεθα φερομένου αὐτοῦ ὀξέως πρὸς πᾶν μέρος τῆς θαλάττης. ἐπεὶ δὲ ἤδη ἐθάδες τῇ
480 διατριβῇ ἐγιγνόμεθα, λαβὼν ἑπτὰ τῶν ἑταίρων ἐβάδιζον ἐς τὴν ὕλην, περισκέψασθαι τὰ πάντα βουλόμενος. οὔπω δὲ πέντε ὅλους διελθὼν σταδίους εὗρον ἱερὸν Ποσειδῶνος, ὡς ἐδήλου ἡ ἐπιγραφὴ, καὶ μετ' οὐ πολὺ καὶ τάφους πολλοὺς καὶ στήλας ἐπ' αὐτῶν, πλησίον τε πηγὴν ὕδατος
485 διαυγοῦς· ἔτι δὲ καὶ κυνὸς ὑλακὴν ἠκούομεν καὶ καπνὸς ἐφαίνετο πόρρωθεν καί τινα καὶ ἔπαυλιν εἰκάζομεν.

We meet an old man and his son, who have lived here twenty-seven years. After hearing our story the old man tells his own, and describes the region in which we are.

Σπουδῇ οὖν βαδίζοντες ἐφιστάμεθα πρεσβύτῃ καὶ νεανίσκῳ, μάλα προθύμως πρασιάν τινα ἐργαζομένοις καὶ ὕδωρ ἀπὸ τῆς πηγῆς ἐπ' αὐτὴν διοχετεύουσιν· ἡσθέν-
490 τες οὖν ἅμα καὶ φοβηθέντες ἔστημεν· κἀκεῖνοι δὲ, ταὐτὸν ἡμῖν ὡς τὸ εἰκὸς παθόντες, ἄναυδοι παρεστήκεσαν· χρόνῳ δὲ ὁ πρεσβύτης ἔφη, "Τίνες ἄρα ὑμεῖς ἐστὲ, ὦ ξένοι; πότερον," ἔφη, "τῶν ἐναλίων δαιμόνων, ἢ ἄνθρωποι δυστυχεῖς ἡμῖν παραπλήσιοι; καὶ γὰρ ἡμεῖς ἄνθρωποι
495 ὄντες καὶ ἐν γῇ τραφέντες νῦν θαλάττιοι γεγόναμεν, καὶ συννηχόμεθα τῷ περιέχοντι τούτῳ θηρίῳ, οὐδ' ἃ πάσχομεν ἀκριβῶς εἰδότες. τεθνάναι μὲν γὰρ εἰκάζομεν, ζῆν δὲ πιστεύομεν." πρὸς ταῦτα κἀγὼ εἶπον· "Καὶ

ἡμεῖς τοι ἄνθρωποι νεήλυδες ἐσμὲν, ὦ πάτερ, αὐτῷ σκάφει πρώην καταποθέντες. προήλθομεν δὲ νῦν βουλόμενοι μαθεῖν τὰ ἐν τῇ ὕλῃ ὡς ἔχει. πολλὴ γάρ τις καὶ λάσιος ἐφαίνετο. δαίμων δέ τις, ὡς ἔοικεν, ἡμᾶς ἤγαγε, σέ τε ὀψομένους καὶ εἰσομένους ὅτι μὴ μόνοι ἐν τῷδε καθείργμεθα τῷ θηρίῳ· ἀλλὰ φράσον ἡμῖν τὴν σεαυτοῦ τύχην, ὅστις τε ὢν καὶ ὅπως δεῦρο εἰσῆλθες." ὁ δὲ οὐ πρότερον ἔφη ἐρεῖν οὐδὲ πεύσεσθαι παρ' ἡμῶν, πρὶν ξενίων τῶν παρόντων μεταδοῦναι· καὶ λαβὼν ἡμᾶς ἦγεν ἐπὶ τὴν οἰκίαν, (ἐπεποίητο δὲ αὐτάρκη, καὶ στιβάδας ἐνῳκοδόμητο, καὶ τἄλλα ἐξήρτιστο·) παραθεὶς δὲ ἡμῖν λάχανά τε καὶ ἀκρόδρυα καὶ ἰχθῦς ἔτι δὲ καὶ οἶνον ἐγχέας, ἐπειδὴ ἱκανῶς ἐκορέσθημεν, ἐπυνθάνετο ἃ ἐπεπόνθειμεν· κἀγὼ πάντα ἑξῆς διηγησάμην, τόν τε χειμῶνα καὶ τὰ ἐν τῇ νήσῳ καὶ τὸν ἐν τῷ ἀέρι πλοῦν καὶ τὸν πόλεμον καὶ τἄλλα, μέχρι τῆς ἐς τὸ κῆτος καταδύσεως. ὁ δ' ὑπερθαυμάσας καὶ αὐτὸς ἐν μέρει τὰ καθ' αὑτὸν διεξῄει, λέγων, "Τὸ μὲν γένος εἰμὶ, ὦ ξένοι, Κύπριος· ὁρμηθεὶς δὲ κατ' ἐμπορίαν ἀπὸ τῆς πατρίδος μετὰ παιδὸς, ὃν ὁρᾶτε, καὶ ἄλλων πολλῶν οἰκετῶν ἔπλεον εἰς Ἰταλίαν, ποικίλον φόρτον κομίζων ἐπὶ νεὼς μεγάλης, ἣν ἐπὶ στόματι τοῦ κήτους διαλελυμένην ἴσως ἑωράκατε. μέχρι μὲν οὖν Σικελίας εὐτυχῶς διεπλεύσαμεν· ἐκεῖθεν δὲ ἁρπασθέντες ἀνέμῳ σφοδρῷ τριταῖοι ἐς τὸν Ὠκεανὸν ἀπηνείχθημεν, ἔνθα τῷ κήτει περιτυχόντες καὶ αὔτανδροι καταποθέντες δύο ἡμεῖς, τῶν ἄλλων ἀποθανόντων, ἐσώθημεν. θάψαντες δὲ τοὺς ἑταίρους καὶ ναὸν τῷ Ποσειδῶνι δειμάμενοι τουτονὶ τὸν βίον ζῶμεν, λάχανα μὲν κηπεύοντες ἰχθῦς δὲ σιτούμενοι καὶ ἀκρόδρυα. πολλὴ δὲ ὡς ὁρᾶτε ἡ ὕλη, καὶ μὴν καὶ ἀμπέλους ἔχει πολλὰς, ἀφ' ὧν ἥδιστος οἶνος γίγνεται· καὶ τὴν πηγὴν δὲ

530 ἴσως εἴδετε καλλίστου καὶ ψυχροτάτου ὕδατος. εὐνὴν δὲ ἀπὸ τῶν φύλλων ποιούμεθα καὶ πῦρ ἄφθονον καίομεν, καὶ ὄρνεα δὲ θηρεύομεν τὰ εἰσπετόμενα καὶ ζῶντας ἰχθῦς ἀγρεύομεν ἐξιόντες ἐπὶ τὰ βραγχία τοῦ θηρίου, ἔνθα καὶ λουόμεθα, ὁπόταν ἐπιθυμήσωμεν. καὶ μὴν
535 καὶ λίμνη οὐ πόρρω ἐστὶν ἁλμυρὰ, σταδίων εἴκοσι τὴν περίμετρον, ἰχθῦς ἔχουσα παντοδαπούς· ἐν ᾗ καὶ νηχόμεθα καὶ πλέομεν ἐπὶ σκάφους μικροῦ, ὃ ἐγὼ ἐναυπηγησάμην. ἔτη δὲ ἡμῖν ἐστι τῆς καταπόσεως ταῦτα ἑπτὰ καὶ εἴκοσι.

We hear of other inhabitants besides ourselves, who are said to be unpleasant neighbours. A council of war.

540 Καὶ τὰ μὲν ἄλλα ἴσως φέρειν ἐδυνάμεθα· οἱ δὲ γείτονες ἡμῶν καὶ πάροικοι σφόδρα χαλεποὶ καὶ βαρεῖς εἰσιν, ἄμικτοί τε ὄντες καὶ ἄγριοι." "Ἦ γὰρ," ἔφην ἐγὼ, "καὶ ἄλλοι τινές εἰσιν ἐν τῷ κήτει;" "Πολλοὶ μὲν οὖν," ἔφη, "καὶ ἄξενοι, καὶ τὰς μορφὰς ἀλλόκοτοι. τὰ μὲν
545 γὰρ ἑσπέρια καὶ οὐραῖα τῆς ὕλης Ταριχᾶνες οἰκοῦσιν, ἔθνος ἐγχελυωπὸν καὶ καραβοπρόσωπον, μάχιμον καὶ θρασὺ καὶ ὠμοφάγον· τὰ δὲ τῆς ἑτέρας πλευρᾶς, κατὰ τὸν δεξιὸν τοῖχον, Τριτωνομένδητες, τὰ μὲν ἄνω ἀνθρώποις ἐοικότες τὰ δὲ κάτω τοῖς γαλεώταις· ἧττον
550 μέντοι ἄδικοί εἰσι τῶν ἄλλων· τὰ λαιὰ δὲ Καρκινόχειρες καὶ Θυννοκέφαλοι, συμμαχίαν τε καὶ φιλίαν πρὸς ἑαυτοὺς πεποιημένοι· τὴν δὲ μεσόγαιαν νέμονται Παγουρίδαι καὶ Ψηττόποδες, γένος μάχιμον καὶ δρομικώτατον· τὰ ἑῷα δὲ πρὸς αὐτῷ τῷ στόματι τὰ πολλὰ μὲν ἔρημά
555 ἐστι, προσκλυζόμενα τῇ θαλάττῃ. ὅμως δὲ ἐγὼ ταῦτα ἔχω, φόρον τοῖς Ψηττόποσιν ὑποτελῶν ἑκάστου ἔτους ὄστρεα πεντακόσια. τοιαύτη μὲν ἡ χώρα ἐστίν· ἡμᾶς

δὲ χρὴ ὁρᾶν ὅπως δυνησόμεθα τοσούτοις ἔθνεσι μάχεσθαι, καὶ ὅπως βιοτεύσομεν." "Πόσοι δ'," ἔφην ἐγὼ, "οὗτοι πάντες εἰσί;" "Πλείους," ἔφη, "τῶν χιλίων." "Ὅπλα 560 δὲ τίνα εἰσὶν αὐτοῖς;" "Οὐδὲν," ἔφη, "πλὴν ὀστᾶ τῶν ἰχθύων." "Οὐκοῦν," ἔφην ἐγὼ, "ἄριστ' ἂν ἔχοι διὰ μάχης ἐλθεῖν αὐτοῖς, ἅτε οὖσιν ἀνόπλοις, αὐτούς γε ὡπλισμένους. εἰ γὰρ κρατήσομεν αὐτῶν, ἀδεῶς τολοιπὸν οἰκήσομεν." ἔδοξε ταῦτα, καὶ ἀπελθόντες ἐπὶ ναῦν 565 παρεσκευαζόμεθα.

After two days' conflict our enemies are exterminated or driven out, and we are left in undisturbed possession.

Αἰτία δὲ τοῦ πολέμου ἔμελλεν ἔσεσθαι τοῦ φόρου ἡ οὐκ ἀπόδοσις, ἤδη τῆς προθεσμίας ἐνεστώσης. καὶ δὴ οἱ μὲν ἔπεμπον τὸν δασμὸν ἀπαιτοῦντες· ὁ δὲ ὑπεροπτικῶς ἀποκρινάμενος ἀπεδίωξε τοὺς ἀγγέλους. πρῶτοι 570 οὖν οἱ Ψηττόποδες καὶ οἱ Παγουρίδαι χαλεπαίνοντες τῷ Σκινθάρῳ (τοῦτο γὰρ ἐκαλεῖτο) μετὰ πολλοῦ θορύβου ἐπῄεσαν. ἡμεῖς δὲ, τὴν ἔφοδον ὑποπτεύοντες, ἐξοπλισάμενοι ἀνεμένομεν, λόχον τινὰ προτάξαντες ἀνδρῶν πέντε καὶ εἴκοσιν. προείρητο δὲ αὐτοῖς ἐν τῇ ἐνέδρᾳ, 575 ἐπειδὰν ἴδωσι παρεληλυθότας τοὺς πολεμίους, ἐπανίστασθαι· καὶ οὕτως ἐποίησαν. ἐπαναστάντες γὰρ κατόπιν ἔκοπτον αὐτοὺς, καὶ ἡμεῖς δὲ καὶ αὐτοὶ, πέντε καὶ εἴκοσι τὸν ἀριθμὸν ὄντες (καὶ γὰρ καὶ ὁ Σκίνθαρος καὶ ὁ παῖς αὐτοῦ συνεστρατεύοντο), ἠντιάζομεν, καὶ 580 συμμίξαντες θυμῷ καὶ ῥώμῃ διεκινδυνεύομεν. τέλος δὲ τροπὴν αὐτῶν ποιησάμενοι κατεδιώξαμεν ἄχρι πρὸς τοὺς φωλεούς. ἀπέθανον δὲ τῶν μὲν πολεμίων ἑβδομήκοντα καὶ ἑκατὸν ἡμῶν δὲ εἷς καὶ ὁ κυβερνήτης, τρίγλης πλευρᾷ διαπαρεὶς τὸ μετάφρενον. ἐκείνην μὲν οὖν τὴν 585 ἡμέραν καὶ τὴν νύκτα ἐπηυλισάμεθα τῇ μάχῃ καὶ τρόπαιον ἐστήσαμεν, ῥάχιν ξηρὰν δελφῖνος ἀναπήξαντες. τῇ ὑστεραίᾳ δὲ καὶ οἱ ἄλλοι αἰσθόμενοι παρῆσαν, τὸ μὲν δεξιὸν κέρας ἔχοντες οἱ Ταριχᾶνες (ἡγεῖτο δὲ αὐτῶν 590 Πήλαμος) τὸ δ' εὐώνυμον οἱ Θυννοκέφαλοι τὸ μέσον δὲ οἱ Καρκινόχειρες. οἱ γὰρ Τριτωνομένδητες τὴν ἡσυχίαν ἦγον οὐδετέροις συμμαχεῖν προαιρούμενοι. ἡμεῖς δὲ προαπαντήσαντες αὐτοῖς περὶ τὸ Ποσειδώνιον προσεμίξαμεν, πολλῇ βοῇ χρώμενοι. ἀντήχει δὲ τὸ κῆτος ὥσπερ 595 τὰ σπήλαια. τρεψάμενοι δὲ αὐτοὺς, ἅτε γυμνήτας ὄντας, καὶ καταδιώξαντες ἐς τὴν ὕλην τὸ λοιπὸν ἐπεκρατοῦμεν τῆς γῆς. καὶ μετ' οὐ πολὺ κήρυκας ἀποστείλαντες νεκρούς τε ἀνῃροῦντο καὶ περὶ φιλίας διελέγοντο. ἡμῖν δὲ οὐκ ἐδόκει σπένδεσθαι· ἀλλὰ τῇ ὑστεραίᾳ χωρήσαν-600 τες ἐπ' αὐτοὺς πάντας ἄρδην ἐξεκόψαμεν, πλὴν τῶν Τριτωνομενδήτων. οὗτοι δὲ ὡς εἶδον τὰ γιγνόμενα, διαδράντες ἐκ τῶν βραγχίων ἀφῆκαν αὐτοὺς εἰς τὴν θάλατταν. ἡμεῖς δὲ τὴν χώραν ἐπελθόντες, ἔρημον ἤδη οὖσαν τῶν πολεμίων, τὸ λοιπὸν ἀδεῶς κατῳκοῦμεν, τὰ 605 πολλὰ γυμνασίοις τε καὶ κυνηγεσίοις χρώμενοι καὶ ἀμπελουργοῦντες καὶ τὸν καρπὸν συγκομιζόμενοι τὸν ἐκ τῶν δένδρων· καὶ ὅλως ἐῴκειμεν τοῖς ἐν δεσμωτηρίῳ μεγάλῳ καὶ ἀφύκτῳ τρυφῶσι καὶ λελυμένοις.

From the monster's open jaws we descry another marvellous sight; a strange tribe of giants upon floating islands.

Ἐνιαυτὸν μὲν οὖν καὶ μῆνας ὀκτὼ τοῦτον διήγομεν τὸν 610 τρόπον. τῷ δ' ἐννάτῳ μηνὶ, πέμπτῃ ἱσταμένου, περὶ τὴν δευτέραν τοῦ στόματος ἄνοιξιν, (ἅπαξ γὰρ δὴ τοῦτο κατὰ τὴν ὥραν ἑκάστην ἐποίει τὸ κῆτος, ὥστε ἡμᾶς πρὸς τὰς ἀνοίξεις τεκμαίρεσθαι τὰς ὥρας) περὶ οὖν τὴν δευτέραν, ὡς ἔφην, ἄνοιξιν ἄφνω βοή τε πολλὴ καὶ θόρυβος ἠκούετο, ὥσπερ κελεύσματα καὶ εἰρεσίαι. ταραχθέντες οὖν 615 ἀνειρπύσαμεν ἐπ' αὐτὸ τὸ στόμα τοῦ θηρίου, καὶ στάντες ἐνδοτέρω τῶν ὀδόντων καθεωρῶμεν ἁπάντων ὧν ἐγὼ εἶδον θεαμάτων παραδοξότατον, ἄνδρας μεγάλους ὅσον ἡμισταδιαίους τὰς ἡλικίας, ἐπὶ νήσων μεγάλων προσπλέοντας, ὥσπερ ἐπὶ τριηρῶν. οἶδα μὲν ἀπίστοις ἐοι- 620 κότα ἱστορήσων, λέξω δὲ ὅμως. νῆσοι ἦσαν ἐπιμήκεις μὲν οὐ πάνυ δὲ ὑψηλαί, ὅσον ἑκατὸν σταδίων ἑκάστη τὴν περίμετρον. ἐπὶ δ' αὐτῶν ἔπλεον τῶν ἀνδρῶν ἐκείνων ἀμφὶ τοὺς εἴκοσι καὶ ἑκατόν. τούτων δὲ οἱ μὲν παρ' ἑκάτερα τῆς νήσου καθήμενοι ἐφεξῆς ἐκωπηλάτουν, 625 κυπαρίττοις αὐτοκλάδοις μεγάλαις καὶ αὐτοκόμοις, ὡσπερεὶ ἐρετμοῖς. κατόπιν δὲ ἐπὶ τῆς πρύμνης, ὡς ἐδόκει, κυβερνήτης ἐπὶ λόφου ὑψηλοῦ εἱστήκει χαλκοῦν ἔχων πηδάλιον, σταδιαῖον τὸ μῆκος. ἐπὶ δὲ τῆς πρῴρας ὅσον τεσσαράκοντα ὡπλισμένοι αὐτῶν ἐμάχοντο, πάντα ἐοι- 630 κότες ἀνθρώποις, πλὴν τῆς κόμης. αὕτη δὲ πῦρ ἦν καὶ ἐκαίετο, ὥστε οὐδὲ κορύθων ἐδέοντο. ἀντὶ δὲ ἱστίων ὁ ἄνεμος ἐμπίπτων τῇ ὕλῃ, πολλῇ οὔσῃ ἐν ἑκάστῃ, ἐκόλπου τε αὐτὴν καὶ ἔφερε τὴν νῆσον, ᾗ ἐθέλοι ὁ κυβερνήτης. κελευστὴς δ' ἐφειστήκει αὐτοῖς, καὶ πρὸς τὴν εἰ- 635 ρεσίαν ὀξέως ἐκινοῦντο, ὥσπερ τὰ μακρὰ τῶν πλοίων.

The Battle of the Islands.

Τὸ μὲν οὖν πρῶτον δύο ἢ τρεῖς ἑωρῶμεν· ὕστερον δ' ἐφάνησαν ὅσον ἑξακόσιοι· καὶ διαστάντες ἐπολέμουν καὶ ἐναυμάχουν. πολλαὶ μὲν οὖν ἀντίπρωροι συνηράσσοντο ἀλλήλαις πολλαὶ δὲ καὶ ἐμβληθεῖσαι κατεδύοντο, αἱ δὲ 640 συμπλεκόμεναι καρτερῶς διηγωνίζοντο, καὶ οὐ ῥᾳδίως ἀπελύοντο. οἱ γὰρ ἐπὶ τῆς πρῴρας τεταγμένοι πᾶσαν

ἐπεδείκνυντο προθυμίαν ἐπεμβαίνοντες καὶ ἀναιροῦντες· ἐζώγρει δὲ οὐδείς. ἀντὶ δὲ χειρῶν σιδηρῶν πολύποδας
645 μεγάλους ἐκδεδεμένους ἀλλήλοις ἐπερρίπτουν· οἱ δὲ περιπλεκόμενοι τῇ ὕλῃ κατεῖχον τὴν νῆσον. ἔβαλλον μέντοι καὶ ἐτίτρωσκον ὀστρέοις τε ἁμαξοπληθέσι καὶ σπόγγοις πλεθριαίοις. ἡγεῖτο δὲ τῶν μὲν Αἰολοκένταυρος τῶν δὲ Θαλασσοπότης· καὶ μάχη αὐτοῖς ἐγεγένητο,
650 ὡς ἐδόκει, λείας ἕνεκα. ἐλέγετο γὰρ ὁ Θαλασσοπότης πολλὰς ἀγέλας δελφίνων τοῦ Αἰολοκενταύρου ἐληλακέναι, ὡς ἦν ἀκούειν ἐπικαλούντων ἀλλήλοις καὶ τὰ ὀνόματα τῶν βασιλέων ἐπιβοωμένων. τέλος δὲ νικῶσιν οἱ τοῦ Αἰολοκενταύρου, καὶ νήσους τῶν πολεμίων καταδύουσιν
655 ἀμφὶ τὰς πεντήκοντα καὶ ἑκατόν· καὶ ἄλλας τρεῖς λαμβάνουσιν αὐτοῖς ἀνδράσιν· αἱ δὲ λοιπαὶ πρύμναν κρουσάμεναι ἔφυγον. οἱ δὲ μέχρι τινὸς διώξαντες, ἐπειδὴ ἑσπέρα ἦν, τραπόμενοι πρὸς τὰ ναυάγια, τῶν πλείστων ἐπεκράτησαν καὶ τὰ ἑαυτῶν ἀνείλοντο. καὶ γὰρ ἐκεί-
660 νων κατέδυσαν νῆσοι οὐκ ἐλάττους τῶν ὀγδοήκοντα. ἔστησαν δὲ καὶ τρόπαιον τῆς νησομαχίας, ἐπὶ τῇ κεφαλῇ τοῦ κήτους μίαν τῶν πολεμίων νήσων ἀνασταυρώσαντες. ἐκείνην μὲν οὖν τὴν νύκτα περὶ τὸ θηρίον ηὐλίσαντο, ἐξάψαντες αὐτοῦ τὰ ἀπόγεια καὶ ἐπ' ἀγκυρῶν πλησίον
665 ὁρμισάμενοι. καὶ γὰρ ἀγκύραις ἐχρῶντο μεγάλαις ὑαλίναις καρτεραῖς. τῇ ὑστεραίᾳ δὲ θύσαντες ἐπὶ τοῦ κήτους καὶ τοὺς οἰκείους θάψαντες ἐπ' αὐτοῦ ἀπέπλεον ἡδόμενοι, καὶ ὥσπερ παιᾶνας ᾄδοντες. ταῦτα μὲν τὰ κατὰ τὴν νησομαχίαν γιγνόμενα.

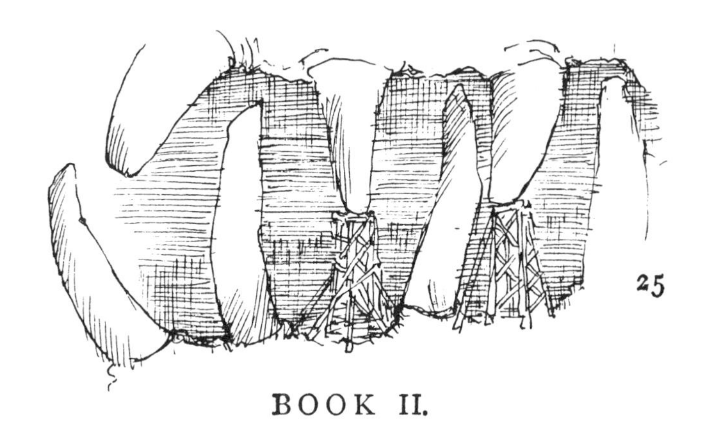

BOOK II.

Tired of our long imprisonment we contrive a means of escape, and launch our vessel once more on the open sea.

Τὸ δ' ἀπὸ τούτου μηκέτι φέρων ἐγὼ τὴν ἐν τῷ κήτει δίαιταν ἀχθόμενός τε τῇ μονῇ μηχανήν τινα ἐζήτουν, δι' ἧς ἂν ἐξελθεῖν γένοιτο. καὶ τὸ μὲν πρῶτον ἔδοξεν ἡμῖν διορύξασι κατὰ τὸν δεξιὸν τοῖχον ἀποδρᾶναι· καὶ ἀρξάμενοι διεκόπτομεν. ἐπειδὴ δὲ προελθόντες ὅσον 5 πέντε σταδίους οὐδὲν ἠνύομεν, τοῦ ὀρύγματος ἐπαυσάμεθα τὴν δὲ ὕλην καῦσαι διέγνωμεν· οὕτω γὰρ ἂν τὸ κῆτος ἀποθανεῖν. εἰ δὲ τοῦτο γένοιτο, ῥᾳδία ἔμελλεν ἡμῖν ἔσεσθαι ἡ ἔξοδος. ἀρξάμενοι οὖν ἀπὸ τῶν οὐραίων ἐκαίομεν· καὶ ἡμέρας μὲν ἑπτὰ καὶ νύκτας ἴσας 10 ἀναισθήτως εἶχε τοῦ καύματος· ὀγδόῃ δὲ καὶ ἐνάτῃ συνίεμεν αὐτοῦ νοσοῦντος· ἀργότερον γοῦν ἀνέχασκε· καὶ εἴποτε ἀναχάνοι, ταχὺ συνέμυε. δεκάτῃ δὲ καὶ ἑνδεκάτῃ τέλεον ἀπενενέκρωτο καὶ δυσῶδες ἦν. τῇ δωδεκάτῃ δὲ μόγις ἐνενοήσαμεν, ὡς, εἰ μή τις χανόντος αὐ- 15 τοῦ ὑποστηρίξειε τοὺς γομφίους ὥστε μηκέτι συγκλεῖσαι, κινδυνεύσομεν κατακλεισθέντες ἐν νεκρῷ αὐτῷ ἀπολέσθαι· οὕτω δὴ τὸ στόμα μεγάλαις δοκοῖς διερείσαντες τὴν ναῦν ἐπεσκευάζομεν, ὕδωρ τε ὡς ἔνι πλεῖστον ἐμβαλλόμενοι καὶ τἄλλα ἐπιτήδεια. κυβερνήσειν δ' ἔμελλεν ὁ 20 Σκίνθαρος. τῇ δ' ἐπιούσῃ τὸ μὲν ἤδη ἐτεθνήκει· ἡμεῖς δ' ἀνελκύσαντες τὸ πλοῖον καὶ διὰ τῶν ἀραιωμάτων διαγαγόντες καὶ ἐκ τῶν ὀδόντων ἐξάψαντες ἠρέμα καθήκαμεν ἐς τὴν θάλατταν· ἐπαναβάντες δ' ἐπὶ τὰ νῶτα καὶ θύσαντες τῷ Ποσειδῶνι αὐτοῦ παρὰ τὸ τρόπαιον 25

ἡμέρας τε τρεῖς ἐπαυλισάμενοι (νηνεμία γὰρ ἦν) τετάρτῃ ἀπεπλεύσαμεν.

We make our way across the Frozen Sea and reach the Island of Cheese.

Ἔνθα δὴ πολλοῖς τῶν ἐκ τῆς ναυμαχίας νεκροῖς ἀπηντῶμεν καὶ προσωκέλλομεν· καὶ τὰ σώματα καταμετροῦν-
30 τες ἐθαυμάζομεν. καὶ ἡμέρας μέν τινας ἐπλέομεν εὐκράτῳ ἀέρι χρώμενοι· ἔπειτα βορέου σφοδροῦ πνεύσαντος μέγα κρύος ἐγένετο, καὶ ὑπ᾽ αὐτοῦ πᾶν ἐπάγη τὸ πέλαγος, οὐκ ἐξεπιπολῆς μόνον ἀλλὰ καὶ ἐς βάθος, ὅσον ἐς τετρακοσίας ὀργυίας· ὥστε καὶ ἀποβάντας διαθέειν
35 ἐπὶ τοῦ κρυστάλλου. ἐπιμένοντος οὖν τοῦ πνεύματος, φέρειν οὐ δυνάμενοι τοιόνδε τι ἐπενοήσαμεν. (ὁ δὲ τὴν γνώμην ἀποφηνάμενος ἦν ὁ Σκίνθαρος). σκάψαντες γὰρ ἐν τῷ ὕδατι σπήλαιον μέγιστον ἐν τούτῳ ἐμείναμεν ἡμέρας τριάκοντα, πῦρ ἀνακαίοντες καὶ σιτούμενοι τοὺς
40 ἰχθῦς· εὑρίσκομεν δὲ αὐτοὺς ἀνορύττοντες. ἐπειδὴ δὲ ἤδη ἐπέλιπε τὰ ἐπιτήδεια, προσελθόντες καὶ τὴν ναῦν πεπηγυῖαν ἀνασπάσαντες καὶ πετάσαντες τὴν ὀθόνην ἐσυρόμεθα ὥσπερ πλέοντες λείως καὶ προσηνῶς, ἐπὶ τοῦ πάγου διολισθαίνοντες. ἡμέρᾳ δὲ πέμπτῃ ἀλέα τε ἤδη
45 ἦν καὶ ὁ πάγος ἐλύετο καὶ ὕδωρ πάντα αὖθις ἐγίγνετο. πλεύσαντες οὖν ὅσον τριακοσίους σταδίους νήσῳ μικρᾷ καὶ ἐρήμῃ προσηνέχθημεν, ἀφ᾽ ἧς ὕδωρ λαβόντες (ἐπελελοίπει γὰρ ἤδη) καὶ δύο ταύρους ἀγρίους κατατοξεύσαντες ἀπεπλεύσαμεν. οἱ δὲ ταῦροι οὗτοι τὰ κέρατα οὐκ
50 ἐπὶ τῆς κεφαλῆς εἶχον, ἀλλ᾽ ὑπὸ τοῖς ὀφθαλμοῖς, ὥσπερ ὁ Μῶμος ἠξίου. μετ᾽ οὐ πολὺ δὲ εἰς πέλαγος ἐνεβαίνομεν, οὐχ ὕδατος ἀλλὰ γάλακτος. καὶ νῆσος ἐν αὐτῷ ἐφαίνετο λευκή, πλήρης ἀμπέλων. ἦν δὲ ἡ νῆσος τυρὸς

μέγιστος, πάνυ συμπεπηγὼς, ὡς ὕστερον ἐμφαγόντες ἐμάθομεν, σταδίων εἰκοσιπέντε τὸ περίμετρον· αἱ δ' 55 ἄμπελοι βοτρύων πλήρεις· οὐ μέντοι οἶνον ἀλλὰ γάλα ἐξ αὐτῶν ἀποθλίβοντες ἐπίνομεν. ἱερὸν δ' ἐν μέσῃ τῇ νήσῳ ἀνῳκοδόμητο Γαλατείας τῆς Νηρηΐδος, ὡς ἐδήλου τὸ ἐπίγραμμα. ὅσον δ' οὖν χρόνον ἐκεῖ ἐμείναμεν ὄψον μὲν ἡ γῆ καὶ σιτίον ὑπῆρχε ποτὸν δὲ τὸ ἐκ τῶν βοτρύων 60 γάλα. βασιλεύειν δὲ τούτων τῶν χωρίων ἐλέγετο Τυρὼ ἡ Σαλμωνέως, μετὰ τὴν ἐντεῦθεν ἀπαλλαγὴν ταύτην παρὰ τοῦ Ποσειδῶνος λαβοῦσα τὴν τιμήν.

The Cork-foot people. The Island of the Blest, with its fragrant smells, its musical birds and breezes.

Μείναντες δὲ ἡμέρας ἐν τῇ νήσῳ πέντε τῇ ἕκτῃ ἐξωρμήσαμεν, αὔρας μέν τινος παραπεμπούσης λειοκύ- 65 μονος δὲ οὔσης τῆς θαλάττης. τῇ ὀγδόῃ δὲ ἡμέρᾳ πλέοντες, οὐκ ἔτι διὰ τοῦ γάλακτος ἀλλ' ἤδη ἐν ἁλμυρῷ καὶ κυανῷ ὕδατι, καθορῶμεν ἀνθρώπους πολλοὺς ἐπὶ τοῦ πελάγους διαθέοντας, ἅπαντα ἡμῖν προσεοικότας καὶ τὰ σώματα καὶ τὰ μεγέθη, πλὴν μόνων τῶν ποδῶν· ταῦτα 70 γὰρ φέλλινα εἶχον· ἀφ' οὗ δὴ οἶμαι καὶ ἐκαλοῦντο Φελλόποδες. ἐθαυμάζομεν οὖν ἰδόντες οὐ βαπτιζομένους, ἀλλ' ὑπερέχοντας τῶν κυμάτων καὶ ἀδεῶς ὁδοιποροῦντας· οἱ δὲ καὶ προσῄεσαν καὶ ἠσπάζοντο ἡμᾶς Ἑλληνικῇ φωνῇ, ἔλεγόν τε εἰς Φελλὼ τὴν αὐτῶν πατρίδα ἐπείγε- 75 σθαι· μέχρι μὲν δή τινος συνωδοιπόρουν ἡμῖν παραθέοντες· εἶτα ἀποτραπόμενοι τῆς ὁδοῦ ἐβάδιζον, εὔπλοιαν ἡμῖν ἐπευξάμενοι. μετ' ὀλίγον δὲ πολλαὶ νῆσοι ἐφαίνοντο· πλησίον μὲν ἐξ ἀριστερῶν ἡ Φελλὼ, ἐς ἣν ἐκεῖνοι ἔσ-πευδον, πόλις ἐπὶ μεγάλου καὶ στρογγύλου φελλοῦ 80 κατοικουμένη. πορρωθεν δὲ καὶ μᾶλλον ἐν δεξιᾷ

πέντε μέγισται καὶ ὑψηλόταται, καὶ πῦρ πολὺ ἀπ αὐτῶν ἀνεκαίετο. κατὰ δὲ τὴν πρώραν μία πλατεῖα καὶ ταπεινὴ, σταδίους ἀπέχουσα οὐκ ἐλάττους πεντακοσίων.
85 ἤδη δὲ πλησίον τε ἦμεν, καὶ θαυμαστή τις αὖρα περιέπνευσεν ἡμᾶς, ἡδεῖα καὶ εὐώδης, οἵαν φησὶν ὁ συγγραφεὺς Ἡρόδοτος ἀπόζειν τῆς εὐδαίμονος Ἀραβίας. οἷον γὰρ ἀπὸ ῥόδων καὶ ναρκίσσων καὶ ὑακίνθων καὶ κρίνων καὶ ἴων, ἔτι δὲ μυρρίνης καὶ δάφνης καὶ ἀμπελάνθης, τοιοῦ-
90 τον ἡμῖν τὸ ἡδὺ προσέβαλλεν. ἡσθέντες δὲ τῇ ὀσμῇ καὶ χρηστὰ ἐκ μακρῶν πόνων ἐλπίσαντες κατ' ὀλίγον ἤδη πλησίον τῆς νήσου ἐγιγνόμεθα. ἔνθα δὴ καὶ καθεωρῶμεν λιμένας τε πολλοὺς περὶ πᾶσαν ἀκλύστους καὶ μεγάλους, ποταμούς τε διαυγεῖς ἐξιόντας ἠρέμα ἐς τὴν
95 θάλατταν· ἔτι δὲ λειμῶνας καὶ ὕλας καὶ ὄρνεα μουσικὰ, τὰ μὲν ἐπὶ τῶν ἠϊόνων ᾄδοντα πολλὰ δὲ καὶ ἐπὶ τῶν κλάδων. ἀὴρ δὲ κοῦφος καὶ εὔπνους περιεκέχυτο τὴν χώραν· καὶ αὖραι δέ τινες ἡδεῖαι διαπνέουσαι ἠρέμα τὴν ὕλην διεσάλευον· ὥστε καὶ ἀπὸ τῶν κλάδων κινουμένων
100 τερπνὰ καὶ συνεχῆ μέλη ἀπεσυρίζετο, ἐοικότα τοῖς ἐπ' ἐρημίας αὐλήμασι τῶν πλαγίων αὐλῶν. καὶ μὴν καὶ βοὴ σύμμικτος ἠκούετο ἄθρους, οὐ θορυβώδης, ἀλλ' οἵα γένοιτ' ἂν ἐν συμποσίῳ, τῶν μὲν αὐλούντων, ἄλλων δὲ ἐπαινούντων ἐνίων δὲ κροτούντων πρὸς αὐλὸν ἢ κιθάραν.
105 τούτοις ἅπασι κηλούμενοι κατήχθημεν. ὁρμίσαντες δὲ τὴν ναῦν ἀπεβαίνομεν, τὸν Σκίνθαρον ἐν αὐτῇ καὶ δύο τῶν ἑταίρων ἀπολιπόντες.

We are brought before the king Rhadamanthus for examination, and are permitted to stay awhile.

Προϊόντες δὲ διὰ λειμῶνος εὐανθοῦντος ἐντυγχάνομεν τοῖς φρουροῖς καὶ περιπόλοις· οἱ δὲ δήσαντες ἡμᾶς ῥο-

δίνοις στεφάνοις (οὗτος γὰρ μέγιστος παρ' αὐτοῖς δε- 110
σμός ἐστιν) ἀνῆγον ὡς τὸν ἄρχοντα· παρ' ὧν δὴ καθ'
ὁδὸν ἠκούσαμεν, ὡς ἡ μὲν νῆσος εἴη τῶν Μακάρων προσ-
αγορευομένη ἄρχοι δὲ ὁ Κρὴς Ῥαδάμανθυς. καὶ δὴ
ἀναχθέντες ὡς αὐτὸν ἐν τάξει τῶν δικαζομένων ἔστημεν
τέταρτοι. ἦν δὲ ἡ μὲν πρώτη δίκη περὶ Αἴαντος τοῦ 115
Τελαμῶνος, εἴτε χρὴ αὐτὸν συνεῖναι τοῖς ἥρωσιν εἴτε καὶ
μή· κατηγορεῖτο δὲ αὐτοῦ, ὅτι μεμήνοι καὶ ἑαυτὸν ἀπο-
κτάνοι· τέλος δέ, πολλῶν ῥηθέντων, ὁ Ῥαδάμανθυς
ἀπεφαίνετο νῦν μὲν αὐτὸν πιόμενον τοῦ ἐλλεβόρου πα-
ραδοθῆναι Ἱπποκράτει τῷ Κῴῳ ἰατρῷ, ὕστερον δὲ σω- 120
φρονήσαντα μετέχειν τοῦ συμποσίου. δευτέρα δὲ ἦν
κρίσις ἐρωτική, Θησέως καὶ Μενελάου περὶ τῆς Ἑλένης
διαγωνιζομένων, ποτέρῳ αὐτὴν χρὴ συνοικεῖν. καὶ ὁ
Ῥαδάμανθυς ἐδίκασε Μενελάῳ συνεῖναι αὐτήν, ἅτε καὶ
τοσαῦτα πονήσαντι καὶ κινδυνεύσαντι τοῦ γάμου ἕνεκεν· 125
καὶ γὰρ αὐτῷ Θησεῖ καὶ ἄλλας εἶναι γυναῖκας, τήν τε
Ἀμαζόνα καὶ τὰς τοῦ Μίνωος θυγατέρας. τρίτη δ'
ἐδικάσθη περὶ προεδρίας, Ἀλεξάνδρῳ τε τῷ Φιλίππου
καὶ Ἀννίβᾳ τῷ Καρχηδονίῳ· καὶ ἔδοξε προέχειν ὁ Ἀλέ-
ξανδρος, καὶ θρόνος αὐτῷ ἐτέθη παρὰ Κῦρον τὸν Πέρ- 130
σην, τὸν πρότερον. τέταρτοι δ' ἡμεῖς προσηνέχθημεν·
καὶ ὁ μὲν ἤρετο, τί παθόντες ἔτι ζῶντες ἱεροῦ χωρίου
ἐπιβαίημεν· ἡμεῖς δὲ πάντα ἑξῆς διηγησάμεθα. οὕτω
δὴ μεταστησάμενος ἡμᾶς ἐπὶ πολὺν χρόνον ἐσκέπτετο,
καὶ τοῖς συνέδροις ἐκοινοῦτο περὶ ἡμῶν. συνήδρευον 135
δὲ ἄλλοι τε πολλοὶ καὶ Ἀριστείδης ὁ δίκαιος, ὁ Ἀθηναῖος. ὡς δ' ἔδοξεν αὐτῷ, ἀπεφήνατο τῆς μὲν πολυ-
πραγμοσύνης καὶ τῆς ἀποδημίας, ἐπειδὰν ἀποθάνωμεν,
δοῦναι τὰς εὐθύνας, τὸ δὲ νυνὶ ῥητὸν χρόνον μείναντας
ἐν τῇ νήσῳ καὶ συνδιαιτηθέντας τοῖς ἥρωσιν ἀπελθεῖν. 140

ἔταξε δὲ καὶ τὴν προθεσμίαν τῆς ἐπιδημίας, μὴ πλέον μηνῶν ἑπτά.

Description of the Isle of the Blest and its ravishing joys.

Τοὐντεῦθεν αὐτομάτων ἡμῖν τῶν στεφάνων περιρρυέντων, ἐλελύμεθα καὶ εἰς τὴν πόλιν ἠγόμεθα, εἰς τὸ τῶν
145 Μακάρων συμπόσιον. αὕτη μὲν οὖν ἡ πόλις πᾶσα χρυσῆ, τὸ δὲ τεῖχος περίκειται σμαράγδινον· πύλαι δέ εἰσιν ἑπτὰ, πᾶσαι μονόξυλοι κινναμώμινοι. τὸ μέντοι ἔδαφος τῆς πόλεως καὶ ἡ ἐντὸς τοῦ τείχους γῆ ἐλεφαντίνη. ναοὶ δὲ πάντων θεῶν βηρύλλου λίθου ᾠκοδομη-
150 μένοι· καὶ βωμοὶ ἐν αὐτοῖς μέγιστοι μονόλιθοι ἀμεθύστινοι, ἐφ' ὧν ποιοῦσι τὰς ἑκατόμβας. περὶ δὲ τὴν πόλιν ῥεῖ ποταμὸς μύρου τοῦ καλλίστου, τὸ πλάτος πηχέων ἑκατὸν βασιλικῶν, βάθος δὲ ὥστε νεῖν εὐμαρῶς. λουτρὰ δέ ἐστιν αὐτοῖς, οἶκοι μεγάλοι ὑάλινοι, τῷ
155 κινναμώμῳ ἐγκαιόμενοι. ἀντὶ μέντοι τοῦ ὕδατος ἐν ταῖς πυέλοις δρόσος θερμή ἐστιν. ἐσθῆτι δὲ χρῶνται ἀραχνίοις λεπτοῖς πορφύροις. αὐτοὶ δὲ σώματα μὲν οὐκ ἔχουσιν, ἀλλ' ἀναφεῖς καὶ ἄσαρκοί εἰσι, μορφὴν δὲ καὶ ἰδέαν μόνον ἐμφαίνουσι· καὶ ἀσώματοι ὄντες ὅμως
160 οὖν συνεστᾶσι καὶ κινοῦνται καὶ φρονοῦσι καὶ φωνὴν ἀφιᾶσι· καὶ ὅλως ἔοικε γυμνή τις ἡ ψυχὴ αὐτῶν περιπολεῖν τὴν τοῦ σώματος ὁμοιότητα περικειμένη. εἰ γοῦν μὴ ἅψαιτό τις, οὐκ ἂν ἐλέγξειε μὴ εἶναι σῶμα τὸ ὁρώμενον· εἰσὶ γὰρ ὥσπερ σκιαὶ ὀρθαὶ, οὐ μέλαιναι. γηράσκει
165 δὲ οὐδεὶς, ἀλλ' ἐφ' ἧς ἂν ἡλικίας ἔλθῃ παραμένει. οὐ μὴν οὐδὲ νὺξ παρ' αὐτοῖς γίγνεται οὐδὲ ἡμέρα πάνυ λαμπρά· ἀλλὰ καθάπερ τὸ λυκαυγὲς ἤδη πρὸς ἕω, μηδέπω ἀνατείλαντος ἡλίου, τοιοῦτο φῶς ἐπέχει τὴν γῆν. καὶ μέντοι καὶ ὥραν μίαν ἴσασι τοῦ ἔτους· αἰεὶ γὰρ παρ'

αὐτοῖς ἔαρ ἐστὶ καὶ εἷς ἄνεμος πνεῖ ὁ Ζέφυρος. ἡ δὲ 170
χώρα πᾶσι μὲν ἄνθεσι πᾶσι δὲ φυτοῖς ἡμέροις τε καὶ
σκιεροῖς τέθηλεν· αἱ μὲν γὰρ ἄμπελοι δωδεκάφοροί εἰσι
καὶ κατὰ μῆνα ἕκαστον καρποφοροῦσι· τὰς δὲ ῥοιὰς καὶ
τὰς μηλέας καὶ τὴν ἄλλην ὀπώραν ἔλεγον μὲν εἶναι
τρισκαιδεκάφορον· ἑνὸς γὰρ μηνὸς, τοῦ παρ' αὐτοῖς 175
Μινῴου, δὶς καρποφορεῖν. ἀντὶ δὲ πυροῦ οἱ στάχυες
ἄρτους ἑτοίμους ἐπ' ἄκρου φύουσιν, ὥσπερ μύκητας.
πηγαὶ δὲ περὶ τὴν πόλιν ὕδατος μὲν πέντε καὶ ἑξήκοντα
καὶ τριακόσιαι μέλιτος δὲ ἄλλαι τοσαῦται μύρου δὲ
πεντακόσιαι, μικρότεραι μέντοι αὗται· καὶ ποταμοὶ γά- 180
λακτος ἑπτὰ καὶ οἴνου ὀκτώ.

The banqueting-hall; the feast accompanied with song, and the fountains of Mirth and Laughter.

Τὸ δὲ συμπόσιον ἔξω τῆς πόλεως πεποίηται ἐν τῷ
Ἠλυσίῳ καλουμένῳ πεδίῳ· λειμὼν δέ ἐστι κάλλιστος,
καὶ περὶ αὐτὸν ὕλη παντοία πυκνὴ, ἐπισκιάζουσα τοὺς
κατακειμένους. καὶ στρωμνὴ μὲν ἐκ τῶν ἀνθέων ὑπο- 185
βέβληται· διακονοῦνται δὲ καὶ διαφέρουσιν ἕκαστα οἱ
ἄνεμοι, πλήν γε τοῦ οἰνοχοεῖν. τούτου γὰρ οὐδὲν δέονται,
ἀλλ' ἔστι δένδρα περὶ τὸ συμπόσιον ὑάλινα μεγάλα τῆς
διαυγεστάτης ὑάλου· ὁ καρπὸς δ' ἐστι τούτων τῶν δένδρων ποτήρια παντοῖα καὶ τὰς κατασκευὰς καὶ τὰ μεγέ- 190
θη. ἐπειδὰν οὖν παρίῃ τις ἐς τὸ συμπόσιον, τρυγήσας
ἓν ἢ καὶ δύο τῶν ἐκπωμάτων παρατίθεται, τὰ δὲ αὐτίκα
οἴνου πλήρη γίγνεται· οὕτω μὲν πίνουσιν. ἀντὶ δὲ τῶν
στεφάνων αἱ ἀηδόνες καὶ τἆλλα τὰ μουσικὰ ὄρνεα, ἐκ
τῶν πλησίον λειμώνων τοῖς στόμασιν ἀνθολογοῦντα, κα- 195
τανίφει αὐτοὺς μετ' ᾠδῆς ὑπερπετόμενα. καὶ μὴν καὶ
μυρίζονται ὧδί· νεφέλαι πυκναὶ ἀνασπάσασαι μύρον ἐκ

τῶν πηγῶν καὶ τοῦ ποταμοῦ καὶ ἐπιστᾶσαι ὑπὲρ τὸ
συμπόσιον, ἠρέμα τῶν ἀνέμων ὑποθλιβόντων, ὕουσι λε-
200 πτὸν, ὥσπερ δρόσον. ἐπὶ δὲ τῷ δείπνῳ μουσικῇ τε
καὶ ᾠδαῖς σχολάζουσιν· ᾄδεται δὲ αὐτοῖς τὰ τοῦ Ὁμήρου ἔπη μάλιστα· καὶ αὐτὸς δὲ πάρεστι καὶ συνευωχεῖ-
ται αὐτοῖς ὑπὲρ τὸν Ὀδυσσέα κατακείμενος. οἱ μὲν
οὖν χοροὶ ἐκ παίδων εἰσὶ καὶ παρθένων· ἐξάρχουσι δὲ
205 καὶ συνᾴδουσιν Εὔνομός τε ὁ Λοκρὸς, καὶ Ἀρίων ὁ Λέ-
σβιος καὶ Ἀνακρέων καὶ Στησίχορος· καὶ γὰρ καὶ τοῦτον παρ᾽ αὐτοῖς ἐθεασάμην, ἤδη τῆς Ἑλένης αὐτῷ διηλ-
λαγμένης. ἐπειδὰν δὲ οὗτοι παύσωνται ᾄδοντες, δεύτερος χορὸς παρέρχεται ἐκ κύκνων καὶ χελιδόνων καὶ ἀη-
210 δόνων. ἐπειδὰν δὲ καὶ οὗτοι ᾄσωσι, τότε δὴ πᾶσα ἡ
ὕλη ἐπαυλεῖ, τῶν ἀνέμων καταρχόντων. μέγιστον δὲ
δὴ πρὸς εὐφροσύνην ἐκεῖνο ἔχουσι· πηγαί εἰσι δύο παρὰ
τὸ συμπόσιον, ἡ μὲν γέλωτος ἡ δὲ ἡδονῆς· ἐκ τούτων
ἑκατέρας πάντες ἐν ἀρχῇ τῆς εὐωχίας πίνουσι, καὶ τὸ
215 λοιπὸν ἡδόμενοι καὶ γελῶντες διάγουσι.

Heroes and famous men inhabiting the island. Among them are Socrates and other philosophers; some, however, are conspicuous by their absence.

Βούλομαι δὲ εἰπεῖν καὶ τῶν ἐπισήμων οὕστινας παρ
αὐτοῖς ἐθεασάμην· πάντας μὲν τοὺς ἡμιθέους καὶ τοὺς
ἐπὶ Ἴλιον στρατεύσαντας, πλήν γε δὴ τοῦ Λοκροῦ Αἴαν-
τος· ἐκεῖνον δὲ μόνον ἔφασκον ἐν τῷ τῶν ἀσεβῶν χώρῳ
220 κολάζεσθαι. βαρβάρων δὲ Κύρους τε ἀμφοτέρους καὶ
τὸν Σκύθην Ἀνάχαρσιν καὶ τὸν Θρᾷκα Ζάμολξιν καὶ
Νουμᾶν τὸν Ἰταλιώτην, καὶ μὴν καὶ Λυκοῦργον τὸν Λα-
κεδαιμόνιον καὶ Φωκίωνα καὶ Τέλλον, τοὺς Ἀθηναίους,
καὶ τοὺς σοφοὺς, ἄνευ Περιάνδρου. εἶδον δὲ καὶ Σω-

κράτην τὸν Σωφρονίσκου ἀδολεσχοῦντα μετὰ Νέστορος 225
καὶ Παλαμήδους· περὶ δὲ αὐτὸν ἦσαν Ὑάκινθός τε ὁ
Λακεδαιμόνιος καὶ ὁ Θεσπιεὺς Νάρκισσος καὶ Ὕλας
καὶ ἄλλοι καλοί. καί μοι ἐδόκει ἐρᾶν τοῦ Ὑακίνθου·
τὰ πολλὰ γοῦν ἐκεῖνον διήλεγχεν. ἐλέγετο δὲ χαλεπαί-
νειν αὐτῷ ὁ Ῥαδάμανθυς, καὶ ἠπειληκέναι πολλάκις ἐκ- 230
βαλεῖν αὐτὸν ἐκ τῆς νήσου, ἢν φλυαρῇ καὶ μὴ θέλῃ ἀφεὶς
τὴν εἰρωνείαν εὐωχεῖσθαι. Πλάτων δὲ μόνος οὐ παρῆν,
ἀλλ' ἐλέγετο καὶ αὐτὸς ἐν τῇ ὑπ' αὐτοῦ ἀναπλασθείσῃ
πόλει οἰκεῖν, χρώμενος τῇ πολιτείᾳ καὶ τοῖς νόμοις, οἷς
συνέγραψε. οἱ μέντοι ἀμφ' Ἀριστιππόν τε καὶ Ἐπί- 235
κουρον τὰ πρῶτα παρ' αὐτοῖς ἐφέροντο, ἡδεῖς τε ὄντες
καὶ κεχαρισμένοι καὶ συμποτικώτατοι. παρῆν δὲ καὶ
Αἴσωπος ὁ Φρύξ. τούτῳ δὲ ὅσα καὶ γελωτοποιῷ χρῶνται. Διογένης μέν γε ὁ Σινωπεὺς τοσοῦτον μετέβαλε
τοῦ τρόπου, ὥστε γῆμαι Λαΐδα τὴν ἑταίραν, ὀρχεῖσθαί 240
τε ὑπὸ μέθης πολλάκις ἀνιστάμενον καὶ παροινεῖν. τῶν
δὲ Στωϊκῶν οὐδεὶς παρῆν· ἔτι γὰρ ἐλέγοντο ἀναβαίνειν
τὸν τῆς ἀρετῆς ὄρθιον λόφον. ἠκούομεν δὲ καὶ περὶ
Χρυσίππου, ὅτι οὐ πρότερον αὐτῷ ἐπιβῆναι τῆς νήσου
θέμις πρὶν τὸ τέταρτον ἑαυτὸν ἐλλεβορίσῃ. τοὺς δὲ 245
Ἀκαδημαϊκοὺς ἔλεγον ἐθέλειν μὲν ἐλθεῖν, ἐπέχειν δ' ἔτι
καὶ διασκέπτεσθαι· μηδὲ γὰρ αὐτὸ τοῦτό πως καταλαμ-
βάνειν, εἰ καὶ νῆσός τις τοιαύτη ἐστίν· ἄλλως τε καὶ τὴν
ἐπὶ τοῦ Ῥαδαμάνθυος οἶμαι κρίσιν ἐδεδοίκεσαν, ἅτε καὶ
τὸ κριτήριον αὐτοὶ ἀνῃρηκότες. πολλοὺς δὲ αὐτῶν ἔφα- 250
σκον ὁρμηθέντας ἀκολουθεῖν τοῖς ἀφικνουμένοις, ὑπὸ
νωθείας δὲ ἀπολείπεσθαι μὴ καταλαμβάνοντας, καὶ ἀναστρέφειν ἐκ μέσης τῆς ὁδοῦ. οὗτοι μὲν οὖν ἦσαν οἱ
ἀξιολογώτατοι τῶν παρόντων. τιμῶσι δὲ μάλιστα τὸν
Ἀχιλλέα καὶ μετὰ τοῦτον Θησέα. 255

Homer is induced to give a true account of himself and his works. Arrival of Pythagoras and Empedocles.

Οὔπω δὲ δύο ἢ τρεῖς ἡμέραι διεληλύθησαν καὶ προσελθὼν ἐγὼ Ὁμήρῳ τῷ ποιητῇ, σχολῆς οὔσης ἀμφοῖν, τά τε ἄλλα ἐπυνθανόμην καὶ ὅθεν εἴη, λέγων τοῦτο μάλιστα παρ' ἡμῖν εἰσέτι νῦν ζητεῖσθαι. ὁ δὲ οὐδ' αὐτὸς
160 μὲν ἀγνοεῖν ἔφασκεν, ὡς οἱ μὲν Χῖον οἱ δὲ Σμυρναῖον πολλοὶ δὲ καὶ Κολοφώνιον αὐτὸν νομίζουσιν. εἶναι μέντοι ἔλεγε Βαβυλώνιος, καὶ παρά γε τοῖς πολίταις οὐχ Ὅμηρος ἀλλὰ Τιγράνης καλεῖσθαι· ὕστερον δὲ ὁμηρεύσας παρὰ τοῖς Ἕλλησιν ἀλλάξαι τὴν προσηγορίαν. ἔτι δὲ
165 καὶ περι τῶν ἀθετουμένων στίχων ἐπηρώτων, εἰ ὑπ' ἐκείνου εἰσὶ γεγραμμένοι· καὶ ὃς ἔφασκε πάντας αὐτοῦ εἶναι. κατεγίγνωσκον οὖν τῶν ἀμφὶ τὸν Ζηνόδοτον καὶ Ἀρίσταρχον γραμματικῶν πολλὴν τὴν ψυχρολογίαν. ἐπεὶ δὲ ταῦθ' ἱκανῶς ἀπεκρίνατο, πάλιν αὐτὸν ἠρώτων,
170 τί δή ποτε ἀπὸ τῆς μήνιδος τὴν ἀρχὴν ἐποιήσατο· καὶ ὃς εἶπεν οὕτως ἐπελθεῖν αὐτῷ μηδὲν ἐπιτηδεύσαντι. καὶ μὴν κἀκεῖνο ἐπεθύμουν εἰδέναι, εἰ προτέραν ἔγραψε τὴν Ὀδύσσειαν τῆς Ἰλιάδος, ὡς πολλοί φασιν· ὁ δὲ ἠρνεῖτο. ὅτι μὲν γὰρ οὐδὲ τυφλὸς ἦν, ὃ καὶ αὐτὸ περὶ αὐτοῦ λέ-
175 γουσιν, αὐτίκα ἠπιστάμην· ἑώρα γάρ, ὥστε οὐδὲ πυνθάνεσθαι ἐδεόμην· πολλάκις δὲ καὶ ἄλλοτε τοῦτο ἐποίουν, εἴ ποτε αὐτὸν σχολὴν ἄγοντα ἑώρων. προσιὼν γάρ τι ἐπυνθανόμην αὐτοῦ, καὶ ὃς προθύμως πάντα ἀπεκρίνετο, καὶ μάλιστα μετὰ τὴν δίκην, ἐπειδὴ ἐκράτησεν· ἦν γάρ
180 τις γραφὴ κατ' αὐτοῦ ἐπενηνεγμένη ὕβρεως ὑπὸ Θερσίτου, ἐφ' οἷς αὐτὸν ἐν τῇ ποιήσει ἔσκωψε, καὶ ἐνίκησεν Ὅμηρος Ὀδυσσέως συνηγοροῦντος. κατὰ δὲ τοὺς αὐτοὺς χρόνους τούτους ἀφίκετο καὶ Πυθαγόρας ὁ Σάμιος, ἑπτάκις

ἀλλαγεὶς καὶ ἐν τοσούτοις ζώοις βιοτεύσας καὶ ἐκτελέσας τῆς ψυχῆς τὰς περιόδους· ἦν δὲ χρυσοῦς ὅλον τὸ 285
δεξιὸν ἡμίτομον. καὶ ἐκρίθη μὲν συμπολιτεύεσθαι αὐτοῖς, ἐνεδοιάζετο δὲ ἔτι πότερον Πυθαγόραν ἢ Εὔφορβον
χρὴ αὐτὸν ὀνομάζειν. ὁ μέντοι Ἐμπεδοκλῆς ἦλθε μὲν καὶ οὗτος, περίεφθος καὶ τὸ σῶμα ὅλον ὠπτημένος· οὐ
μὴν παρεδέχθη γε καίτοι πολλὰ ἱκετεύων. 290

Gymnastic and poetic contests. An attempted invasion of the island. The invaders are repulsed, and the heroes celebrate their victory.

Προϊόντος δὲ τοῦ χρόνου ἐνέστη ὁ ἀγὼν, τὰ παρ' αὐτοῖς Θανατούσια. ἠγωνοθέτει δὲ Ἀχιλλεὺς τὸ πέμπτον καὶ Θησεὺς τὸ ἕβδομον. τὰ μὲν οὖν ἄλλα μακρὸν ἂν εἴη λέγειν· τὰ δὲ κεφάλαια τῶν πραχθέντων διηγήσομαι. πάλην μὲν ἐνίκησε Κᾶρος ὁ ἀφ' Ἡρακλέους, 295
Ὀδυσσέα περὶ τοῦ στεφάνου καταγωνισάμενος. πυγμὴ δὲ ἴση ἐγένετο Ἀρείου τε τοῦ Αἰγυπτίου, ὃς ἐν Κορίνθῳ τέθαπται, καὶ Ἐπειοῦ, ἀλλήλοις συνελθόντων. παγκρατίου δὲ οὐ τίθεται ἆθλα παρ' αὐτοῖς. τὸν μέντοι
δρόμον οὐκέτι μέμνημαι ὅστις ἐνίκησε. ποιητῶν δὲ τῇ 300
μὲν ἀληθείᾳ παραπολὺ ἐκράτει Ὅμηρος· ἐνίκησε δὲ ὅμως Ἡσίοδος. τὰ δ' ἆθλα ἦν ἅπασι στέφανος πλακεὶς ἐκ πτερῶν ταωνίων. ἄρτι δὲ τοῦ ἀγῶνος συντετελεσμένου ἠγγέλλοντο οἱ ἐν τῷ χωρίῳ τῶν ἀσεβῶν κολαζόμενοι,
ἀπορρήξαντες τὰ δεσμὰ καὶ τῆς φρουρᾶς ἐπικρατήσαντες, 305
ἐλαύνειν ἐπὶ τὴν νῆσον· ἡγεῖσθαι δὲ αὐτῶν Φάλαρίν τε τὸν Ἀκραγαντῖνον καὶ Βούσιριν τὸν Αἰγύπτιον καὶ Διομήδην τὸν Θρᾷκα καὶ τοὺς περὶ Σκείρωνα καὶ Πιτυοκάμπτην. ὡς δὲ ταῦτ' ἤκουσεν ὁ Ῥαδάμανθυς, ἐκτάσσει
τοὺς ἥρωας ἐπὶ τῆς ἠϊόνος· ἡγεῖτο δὲ Θησεύς τε καὶ 310

Ἀχιλλεὺς καὶ Αἴας ὁ Τελαμώνιος, ἤδη σωφρονῶν. καὶ συμμίξαντες ἐμάχοντο, καὶ ἐνίκησαν οἱ ἥρωες, Ἀχιλλέως τὰ πλεῖστα κατορθώσαντος. ἠρίστευσε δὲ καὶ Σωκράτης ἐπὶ τῷ δεξιῷ ταχθεὶς πολὺ μᾶλλον ἢ ὅτε ζῶν ἐπὶ Δηλίῳ
315 ἐμάχετο. προσιόντων γὰρ τῶν πολεμίων οὐκ ἔφυγε, καὶ τὸ πρόσωπον ἄτρεπτος ἦν· ἐφ' οἷς καὶ ὕστερον ἐξῃρέθη αὐτῷ ἀριστεῖον, καλός τε καὶ μέγας παράδεισος ἐν τῷ προαστείῳ· ἔνθα συγκαλῶν τοὺς ἑταίρους διελέγετο, Νεκρακαδημίαν τὸν τόπον προσαγορεύσας. συλλαβόντες
320 οὖν τοὺς νενικημένους καὶ δήσαντες αὖθις ἀπέπεμψαν ἔτι μᾶλλον κολασθησομένους. ἔγραψε δὲ καὶ ταύτην τὴν μάχην Ὅμηρος, καὶ ἀπιόντι μοι ἔδωκε τὰ βιβλία κομίζειν τοῖς παρ' ἡμῖν ἀνθρώποις· ἀλλ' ὕστερον καὶ ταῦτα μετὰ τῶν ἄλλων ἀπωλέσαμεν. ἦν δὲ ἡ ἀρχὴ τοῦ
325 ποιήματος αὕτη·

Νῦν δέ μοι ἔννεπε, Μοῦσα, μάχην νεκύων ἡρώων.

τότε δ' οὖν κυάμους ἑψήσαντες, ὥσπερ παρ' αὐτοῖς νόμος ἐπειδὰν πόλεμον κατορθώσωσιν, εἱστιῶντο τὰ ἐπινίκια καὶ ἑορτὴν μεγάλην ἦγον· μόνος δὲ ταύτης οὐ
330 μετεῖχε Πυθαγόρας, ἀλλ' ἄσιτος πόρρω ἐκαθέζετο μυσαττόμενος τὴν κυαμοφαγίαν.

Abduction of Helen by one of our party. The fugitives are pursued and brought back.

Ἤδη δὲ μηνῶν ἓξ διεληλυθότων, περὶ μεσοῦντα τὸν ἕβδομον νεώτερα συνίστατο πράγματα. Κινύρας γὰρ ὁ τοῦ Σκινθάρου παῖς, μέγας τε ὢν καὶ καλὸς, ἤρα
335 πολὺν ἤδη χρόνον τῆς Ἑλένης, καὶ αὐτὴ δὲ οὐκ ἀφανὴς ἦν ἐπιμανῶς ἀγαπῶσα τὸν νεανίσκον. πολλάκις γοῦν καὶ διένευον ἀλλήλοις ἐν τῷ συμποσίῳ καὶ προὔ-

πινον, καὶ μόνοι ἐξανιστάμενοι ἐπλανῶντο περὶ τὴν ὕλην. καὶ δὴ ὑπ' ἔρωτος καὶ ἀμηχανίας ἐβουλεύσατο ὁ Κινύρας ἁρπάσας τὴν Ἑλένην φυγεῖν. ἐδόκει δὲ κἀ- 340 κείνῃ ταῦτα, οἴχεσθαι ἀπιόντας ἐς τινὰ τῶν ἐπικειμένων νήσων, ἤτοι ἐς τὴν Φελλὼ ἢ ἐς τὴν Τυρόεσσαν. συνωμότας δὲ πάλαι προσειλήφεσαν τρεῖς τῶν ἑταίρων τῶν ἐμῶν τοὺς θρασυτάτους. τῷ μέντοι πατρὶ οὐκ ἐμήνυσε ταῦτα· ἠπίστατο γὰρ ὑπ' αὐτοῦ κωλυθησόμενος. ὡς δ' 345 ἐδόκει αὐτοῖς, ἐτέλουν τὴν ἐπιβουλήν. καὶ ἐπεὶ νὺξ ἐγένετο, ἐγὼ μὲν οὐ παρῆν, (ἐτύγχανον γὰρ ἐν τῷ συμποσίῳ κοιμώμενος·) οἱ δὲ λαθόντες τοὺς ἄλλους, ἀναλαβόντες τὴν Ἑλένην, ὑπὸ σπουδῆς ἀνήχθησαν. περὶ δὲ τὸ μεσονύκτιον ἀνεγρόμενος ὁ Μενέλαος, ἐπεὶ ἔμαθε τὴν 350 εὐνὴν κενὴν τῆς γυναικὸς, βοήν τε ἵστη καὶ τὸν ἀδελφὸν παραλαβὼν ᾔει πρὸς τὰ βασίλεια τοῦ Ῥαδαμάνθυος. ἡμέρας δ' ὑποφαινούσης ἔλεγον οἱ σκοποὶ καθορᾶν τὴν ναῦν πολὺ ἀπέχουσαν· οὕτω δὴ ἐμβιβάσας ὁ Ῥαδάμανθυς πεντήκοντα τῶν ἡρώων εἰς ναῦν μονόξυλον ἀσφο- 355 δελίνην παρήγγειλε διώκειν· οἱ δὲ ὑπὸ προθυμίας ἐλαύνοντες περὶ μεσημβρίαν καταλαμβάνουσιν αὐτοὺς, ἄρτι ἐς τὸν γαλακτώδη ὠκεανὸν ἐμβαίνοντας, πλησίον τῆς Τυροέσσης· παρὰ τοσοῦτον ἦλθον διαδρᾶναι· καὶ ἀναδησάμενοι τὴν ναῦν ἁλύσει ῥοδίνῃ κατέπλεον. ἡ 360 μὲν οὖν Ἑλένη ἐδάκρυέ τε καὶ ᾐσχύνετο καὶ ἐνεκαλύπτετο· τοὺς δ' ἀμφὶ τὸν Κινύραν ἀνακρίνας πρότερον ὁ Ῥαδάμανθυς, εἴ τινες καὶ ἄλλοι αὐτοῖς συνίσασιν, ὡς οὐδένα εἶπον, ἀπέπεμψεν ἐς τὸν τῶν ἀσεβῶν χῶρον, μαλάχῃ πρότερον μαστιγωθέντας. 365

Our allotted time having expired, we are forced reluctantly to depart. Parting advice and instructions of Rhadamanthus.

Ἐψηφίσαντο δὲ καὶ ἡμᾶς ἐμπροθέσμους ἐκπέμπειν ἐκ τῆς νήσου, τὴν ἐπιοῦσαν ἡμέραν μόνην ἐπιμείναντας. ἐνταῦθα δὴ ἐγὼ ἠνιώμην τε καὶ ἐδάκρυον, οἷα ἔμελλον ἀγαθὰ καταλιπὼν αὖθις πλανηθήσεσθαι. αὐτοὶ μέντοι
370 παρεμυθοῦντο λέγοντες, οὐ πολλῶν ἐτῶν ἀφίξεσθαι πάλιν ὡς αὐτούς· καί μοι ἤδη θρόνον τε καὶ κλισίαν ἐς τοὐπιὸν παρεδείκνυσαν, πλησίον τῶν ἀρίστων. ἐγὼ δὲ προσελθὼν τῷ Ῥαδαμάνθυϊ πολλὰ ἱκέτευον εἰπεῖν τὰ μέλλοντα καὶ ὑποδεῖξαί μοι τὸν πλοῦν. ὁ δὲ ἔφασκεν
375 ἀφίξεσθαι μὲν ἐς τὴν πατρίδα, πολλὰ πρότερον πλανηθέντα καὶ κινδυνεύσαντα· τὸν δὲ χρόνον οὐκέτι τῆς ἐπανόδου προσθεῖναι ἠθέλησεν, ἀλλὰ δὴ καὶ δεικνὺς τὰς πλησίον νήσους (ἐφαίνοντο δὲ πέντε τὸν ἀριθμὸν καὶ ἄλλη ἕκτη πόρρωθεν) ταύτας μὲν εἶναι ἔφασκε τὰς τῶν
380 ἀσεβῶν τὰς πλησίον, "ἀφ' ὧν δὴ," ἔφη, "ὁρᾷς τὸ πολὺ πῦρ καιόμενον· ἕκτη δὲ ἐκείνη τῶν ὀνείρων ἡ πόλις· μετ' αὐτὴν δὲ ἡ τῆς Καλυψοῦς νῆσος, ἀλλ' οὐδέπω σοι φαίνεται. ἐπειδὰν δὲ ταύτας παραπλεύσῃς, τότε δὴ ἀφίξῃ ἐς τὴν μεγάλην ἤπειρον τὴν ἐναντίαν τῇ ὑφ' ὑμῶν
385 κατοικουμένῃ· ἐνταῦθα δὴ πολλὰ παθὼν καὶ ποικίλα ἔθνη διελθὼν καὶ ἀνθρώποις ἀμίκτοις ἐπιδημήσας χρόνῳ ποτὲ ἥξεις εἰς τὴν ἑτέραν ἤπειρον." τοσαῦτ' εἶπε· καὶ ἀνασπάσας ἀπὸ τῆς γῆς μαλάχης ῥίζαν ὤρεξέ μοι, ταύτῃ κελεύσας ἐν τοῖς μεγίστοις κινδύνοις προσεύχεσθαι.
390 παρῄνεσε δὲ καί, εἴ ποτε ἀφικοίμην ἐς τήνδε τὴν γῆν, μήτε πῦρ μαχαίρᾳ σκαλεύειν μήτε θέρμους ἐσθίειν μήτε κόρῃ ὑπὲρ τὰ ὀκτωκαίδεκα ἔτη πλησιάζειν. τούτων γὰρ ἂν μεμνημένον ἐλπίδας ἔχειν τῆς εἰς τὴν νῆσον ἀφίξεως.

τότε μὲν οὖν τὰ περὶ τὸν πλοῦν παρεσκευαζόμην· καὶ ἐπεὶ καιρὸς ἦν, συνειστιώμην αὐτοῖς. τῇ δ' ἐπιούσῃ 395 ἐλθὼν πρὸς Ὅμηρον τὸν ποιητὴν ἐδεήθην αὐτοῦ ποιῆσαί μοι δίστιχον ἐπίγραμμα. καὶ ἐπειδὴ ἐποίησε, στήλην βηρύλλου λίθου ἀναστήσας ἐπέγραψα πρὸς τῷ λιμένι. τὸ δ' ἐπίγραμμα ἦν τοιόνδε·

Λουκιανὸς τάδε πάντα, φίλος μακάρεσσι θεοῖσιν, 400
εἶδέ τε καὶ πάλιν ἦλθεν ἑὴν ἐς πατρίδα γαῖαν.

Ulysses gives me a letter for Calypso. We visit the abode of the damned, full of foul odours and surrounded by mist and gloom. Punishments of the wicked described.

Μείνας δ' ἐκείνην τὴν ἡμέραν τῆς ἐπιούσης ἀνηγόμην, τῶν ἡρώων παραπεμπόντων. ἔνθα μοι καὶ Ὀδυσσεὺς προσελθὼν λάθρα τῆς Πηνελόπης δίδωσιν ἐπιστολὴν ἐς Ὠγυγίαν τὴν νῆσον Καλυψοῖ κομίζειν. συνέπεμψε δέ 405 μοι ὁ Ῥαδάμανθυς τὸν πορθμέα Ναύπλιον, ἵν' εἰ καταχθείημεν ἐς τὰς νήσους μηδεὶς ἡμᾶς συλλάβοι, ἅτε κατ' ἄλλην ἐμπορίαν πλέοντας. ἐπεὶ δὲ τὸν εὐώδη ἀέρα προϊόντες παρεληλύθειμεν, αὐτίκα ἡμᾶς ὀσμή τε δεινὴ διεδέχετο, οἷον ἀσφάλτου καὶ θείου καὶ πίσσης ἅμα 410 καιομένων· καὶ κνίσσα δὲ πονηρὰ καὶ ἀφόρητος, ὥσπερ ἀπ' ἀνθρώπων ὀπτωμένων· καὶ ὁ ἀὴρ ζοφερὸς καὶ ὁμιχλώδης, καὶ κατέσταζεν ἐξ αὐτοῦ δρόσος πιττίνη. καὶ μέντοι καὶ μαστίγων ψόφος ἠκούετο καὶ οἰμωγὴ ἀνθρώπων πολλῶν. ταῖς μὲν οὖν ἄλλαις οὐ προσέσχομεν· ἧς 415 δ' ἐπέβημεν τοιάδε ἦν· κύκλῳ μὲν πᾶσα κρημνώδης καὶ ἀπόξυρος, πέτραις καὶ τράχωσι κατεσκληκυῖα, δένδρον δὲ οὐδὲν οὐδὲ ὕδωρ ἐνῆν· ἀνερπύσαντες δὲ ὅμως κατὰ τοὺς κρημνοὺς προῄειμεν διά τινος ἀκανθώδους καὶ σκολόπων μεστῆς ἀτραποῦ, πολλὴν ἀμορφίαν τῆς χώρας ἐχούσης. 420

ἐλθόντες δὲ ἐπὶ τὴν εἱρκτὴν καὶ τὸ κολαστήριον πρῶτα μὲν τὴν φύσιν τοῦ τόπου ἐθαυμάζομεν. τὸ μὲν γὰρ ἔδαφος αὐτὸ μαχαίραις καὶ σκόλοψι πάντη ἐξηνθήκει, κύκλῳ δὲ ποταμοὶ περιέρρεον, ὁ μὲν βορβόρου ὁ δεύτερος δὲ αἵ-
425 ματος ὁ δὲ ἔνδον πυρὸς, πάνυ μέγας οὗτος καὶ ἀπέρατος· καὶ ἔρρει ὥσπερ ὕδωρ, καὶ ἐκυματοῦτο ὥσπερ θάλαττα· καὶ ἰχθῦς δὲ εἶχε πολλοὺς, τοὺς μὲν δαλοῖς προσεοικότας τοὺς δὲ μικροὺς ἄνθραξι πεπυρωμένοις· ἐκάλουν δὲ αὐτοὺς λυχνίσκους. εἴσοδος δὲ μία στενὴ διὰ πάντων· καὶ
430 πυλωρὸς ἐφειστήκει Τίμων ὁ Ἀθηναῖος. παρελθόντες δὲ ὅμως, τοῦ Ναυπλίου καθηγουμένου, ἑωρῶμεν κολαζομένους, πολλοὺς μὲν βασιλέας πολλοὺς δὲ καὶ ἰδιώτας, ὧν ἐνίους καὶ ἐγνωρίζομεν. εἴδομεν δὲ καὶ τὸν Κινύραν καπνῷ ὑποτυφόμενον. προσετίθεσαν δὲ οἱ περιηγηταὶ καὶ
435 τοὺς ἑκάστων βίους καὶ τὰς αἰτίας, ἐφ' αἷς κολάζονται· καὶ μεγίστας ἁπασῶν τιμωρίας ὑπέμενον οἱ ψευσάμενοί τι παρὰ τὸν βίον καὶ οἱ μὴ τἀληθῆ συγγεγραφότες· ἐν οἷς καὶ Κτησίας ὁ Κνίδιος ἦν καὶ Ἡρόδοτος καὶ ἄλλοι πολλοί. τούτους οὖν ὁρῶν ἐγὼ χρηστὰς εἶχον εἰς τοὐ-
440 πιὸν τὰς ἐλπίδας· οὐδὲν γὰρ ἐμαυτῷ ψεῦδος εἰπόντι συνηπιστάμην.

The Isle of Dreams, and our reception there.

Ταχέως οὖν ἀναστρέψας ἐπὶ τὴν ναῦν (οὐ γὰρ ἐδυνάμην φέρειν τὴν ὄψιν) ἀσπασάμενος τὸν Ναύπλιον ἀπέπλευσα. καὶ μετ' ὀλίγον ἐφαίνετο πλησίον ἡ τῶν
445 ὀνείρων νῆσος, ἀμυδρὰ καὶ ἀσαφὴς ἰδεῖν· ἔπασχε δὲ καὶ αὐτὴ τοῖς ὀνείροις τι παραπλήσιον· ὑπεχώρει γὰρ προσιοῦσιν ἡμῖν καὶ ὑπέφευγε καὶ πορρωτέρω ὑπέβαινε. καταλαβόντες δέ ποτε αὐτὴν καὶ ἐσπλεύσαντες ἐς τὸν Ὕπνον λιμένα προσαγορευόμενον πλησίον τῶν πυλῶν

τῶν ἐλεφαντίνων, ᾗ τὸ τοῦ Ἀλεκτρυόνος ἱερόν ἐστι, περὶ 450
δείλην ὀψίαν ἀπεβαίνομεν· παρελθόντες δ' ἐς τὴν πόλιν
πολλοὺς ὀνείρους καὶ ποικίλους ἑωρῶμεν. πρῶτον δὲ
βούλομαι περὶ τῆς πόλεως εἰπεῖν, ἐπεὶ μηδ' ἄλλῳ τινὶ
γέγραπται περὶ αὐτῆς· ὃς δὲ καὶ μόνος ἐπεμνήσθη
Ὅμηρος οὐ πάνυ ἀκριβῶς συνέγραψε. κύκλῳ μὲν περὶ 455
πᾶσαν αὐτὴν ὕλη ἀνέστηκε, τὰ δένδρα δ' ἐστὶ μήκωνες
ὑψηλαὶ καὶ μανδραγόραι, καὶ ἐπ' αὐτῶν πολύ τι πλῆθος
νυκτερίδων· τοῦτο γὰρ μόνον ἐν τῇ νήσῳ γίγνεται
ὄρνεον. ποταμὸς δὲ παραρρέει πλησίον, ὑπ' αὐτῶν καλούμενος
Νυκτιπόρος, καὶ πηγαὶ δύο παρὰ ταῖς πύλαις· 460
ὀνόματα καὶ ταύταις τῇ μὲν Νήγρετος τῇ δὲ Παννυχία·
ὁ δὲ περίβολος τῆς πόλεως ὑψηλός τε καὶ ποικίλος,
Ἴριδι τὴν χροὰν ὁμοιότατος· πύλαι μέντοι ἔπεισιν, οὐ
δύο, καθάπερ Ὅμηρος εἴρηκεν, ἀλλὰ τέτταρες· δύο μὲν
πρὸς τὸ τῆς Βλακείας πεδίον ἀποβλέπουσαι, ἡ μὲν 465
σιδηρᾶ ἡ δὲ ἐκ κεράμου πεποιημένη, καθ' ἃς ἐλέγοντο
ἀποδημεῖν αὐτῶν οἵ τε φοβεροὶ καὶ φονικοὶ καὶ ἀπηνεῖς·
δύο δὲ πρὸς τὸν λιμένα καὶ τὴν θάλατταν, ἡ μὲν κερατίνη
ἡ δέ, καθ' ἣν ἡμεῖς παρήλθομεν, ἐλεφαντίνη.
εἰσιόντι δ' ἐς τὴν πόλιν ἐν δεξιᾷ μέν ἐστι τὸ Νυκτῷον· 470
σέβουσι γὰρ θεῶν ταύτην μάλιστα καὶ τὸν Ἀλεκτρύονα·
ἐκείνῳ δὲ πλησίον τοῦ λιμένος τὸ ἱερὸν πεποίηται. ἐν
ἀριστερᾷ δὲ τὰ τοῦ Ὕπνου βασίλεια. οὗτος γὰρ δὴ
ἄρχει παρ' αὐτοῖς σατράπας δύο καὶ ὑπάρχους πεποιημένος,
Ταραξίωνά τε τὸν Ματαιογένους καὶ Πλουτοκλέα 475
τὸν Φαντασίωνος. ἐν μέσῃ δὲ τῇ ἀγορᾷ πηγή τίς ἐστιν,
ἣν καλοῦσι Καρεῶτιν· καὶ πλησίον ναοὶ δύο, Ἀπάτης
καὶ Ἀληθείας· ἔνθα καὶ τὸ ἄδυτόν ἐστιν αὐτοῖς καὶ τὸ
μαντεῖον, οὗ προειστήκει προφητεύων Ἀντιφῶν ὁ τῶν
ὀνείρων ὑποκριτής, ταύτης παρὰ τοῦ Ὕπνου λαχὼν τῆς 480

τιμῆς. αὐτῶν μέντοι τῶν ὀνείρων οὔτε φύσις οὔτε ἰδέα
ἡ αὐτή· ἀλλ' οἱ μὲν μακροί τε ἦσαν καὶ μαλακοὶ καὶ
καλοὶ καὶ εὐειδεῖς, οἱ δὲ σκληροὶ καὶ μικροὶ καὶ ἄμορφοι,
καὶ οἱ μὲν χρύσεοι, ὡς ἐδόκουν, οἱ δὲ ταπεινοί τε καὶ
485 εὐτελεῖς. ἦσαν δ' ἐν αὐτοῖς καὶ πτερωτοί τινες καὶ
τερατώδεις, καὶ ἄλλοι καθάπερ ἐς πομπὴν διεσκευασμέ-
νοι, οἱ μὲν ἐς βασιλέας οἱ δὲ καὶ ἐς θεοὺς οἱ δ' ἐς ἄλλα
τοιαῦτα κεκοσμημένοι. πολλοὺς δὲ αὐτῶν καὶ ἐγνωρί-
σαμεν πάλαι παρ' ἡμῖν ἑωρακότες· οἱ δὲ καὶ προσῄεσαν
490 καὶ ἠσπάζοντο, ὡς ἂν καὶ συνήθεις ὑπάρχοντες· καὶ
παραλαβόντες ἡμᾶς καὶ κατακοιμίσαντες πάνυ λαμπρῶς
καὶ δεξιῶς ἐξένιζον, τήν τε ἄλλην ὑποδοχὴν μεγαλοπρεπῆ
παρασκευάσαντες καὶ ὑπισχνούμενοι βασιλέας τε ποιή-
σειν καὶ σατράπας. ἔνιοι δὲ καὶ ἀπῆγον ἡμᾶς ἐς τὰς
495 πατρίδας καὶ τοὺς οἰκείους ἐπεδείκνυον, καὶ αὐθημερὸν
ἐπανῆγον.

The Island of Ogygia. Calypso receives the letter of Ulysses, which affects her deeply.

Ἡμέρας μὲν οὖν τριάκοντα καὶ ἴσας νύκτας παρ'
αὐτοῖς ἐμείναμεν, καθεύδοντες καὶ εὐωχούμενοι. ἔπειτα
δὲ ἄφνω βροντῆς μεγάλης καταρραγείσης, ἀνεγρόμενοι
500 καὶ ἀναθορόντες, ἀνήχθημεν ἐπισιτισάμενοι. τριταῖοι δ'
ἐκεῖθεν τῇ Ὠγυγίᾳ νήσῳ προσσχόντες ἀποβαίνομεν.
πρότερον δ' ἐγὼ λύσας τὴν ἐπιστολὴν ἀνεγίγνωσκον τὰ
γεγραμμένα. ἦν δὲ τοιάδε· "ΟΔΥΣΣΕΥΣ ΚΑΛΥΨΟΙ
χαίρειν. ἴσθι με, ὡς τὰ πρῶτα ἐξέπλευσα παρὰ σοῦ
505 τὴν σχεδίαν κατασκευασάμενος, ναυαγίᾳ χρησάμενον καὶ
μόλις ὑπὸ Λευκοθέας διασωθέντα εἰς τὴν τῶν Φαιάκων
χώραν, ὑφ' ὧν ἐς τὴν οἰκείαν ἀποπεμφθεὶς κατέλαβον
πολλοὺς τῆς γυναικὸς μνηστῆρας ἐν τοῖς ἡμετέροις

τρυφῶντας. ἀποκτείνας δὲ ἅπαντας ὕστερον ὑπὸ Τηλε-
γόνου τοῦ ἐκ Κίρκης μοι γενομένου ἀνηρέθην. καὶ νῦν 510
εἰμι ἐν τῇ Μακάρων νήσῳ, πάνυ μετανοῶν ἐπὶ τῷ καταλιπεῖν τὴν παρὰ σοὶ δίαιταν, καὶ τὴν ὑπὸ σοῦ προτει-
νομένην ἀθανασίαν. ἢν οὖν καιροῦ λάβωμαι, ἀποδρὰς
ἀφίξομαι πρὸς σέ." ταῦτα μὲν ἐδήλου ἡ ἐπιστολή, καὶ
περὶ ἡμῶν, ὅπως ξενισθείημεν. ἐγὼ δὲ προελθὼν ὀλίγον 515
ἀπὸ θαλάττης εὗρον τὸ σπήλαιον τοιοῦτον οἷον Ὅμηρος
εἶπε, καὶ αὐτὴν ταλασιουργοῦσαν. ὡς δὲ τὴν ἐπιστολὴν
ἔλαβε καὶ ἐπελέξατο, πρῶτα μὲν ἐπιπολὺ ἐδάκρυεν·
ἔπειτα δὲ παρεκάλει ἡμᾶς ἐπὶ ξενίαν καὶ εἱστία λαμπρῶς, καὶ περὶ τοῦ Ὀδυσσέως ἐπυνθάνετο καὶ περὶ τῆς 520
Πηνελόπης, ὁποία τε εἴη τὴν ὄψιν, καὶ ει σωφρονοίη,
καθάπερ Ὀδυσσεὺς πάλαι περὶ αὐτῆς ἐκόμπαζε· καὶ
ἡμεῖς τοιαῦτα ἀπεκρινόμεθα, ἐξ ὧν εἰκάζομεν εὐφρανεῖ-
σθαι αὐτήν.

Other strange monsters; the Pumpkin-pirates, the Nutshell-mariners, and riders on dolphins.

Τότε μὲν οὖν ἀπελθόντες ἐπὶ τὴν ναῦν πλησίον ἐπὶ 525
τῆς ἠϊόνος ἐκοιμήθημεν. ἕωθεν δὲ ἀνηγόμεθα, σφοδρό-
τερον κατιόντος τοῦ πνεύματος. καὶ δὴ χειμασθέντες
ἡμέρας δύο τῇ τρίτῃ περιπίπτομεν τοῖς Κολοκυνθοπειρα-
ταῖς. ἄνθρωποι δέ εἰσιν οὗτοι ἄγριοι, ἐκ τῶν πλησίον
νήσων λῃστεύοντες τοὺς παραπλέοντας. τὰ πλοῖα δ' 530
ἔχουσι μεγάλα κολοκύνθινα, τὸ μῆκος πηχέων ἑξήκοντα.
ἐπειδὰν γὰρ ξηρανθῶσι, κοιλάναντες αὐτὴν καὶ ἐξελόντες
τὴν ἐντεριώνην ἐμπλέουσιν, ἱστοῖς μὲν χρώμενοι καλα-
μίνοις ἀντὶ δὲ τῆς ὀθόνης τῷ φύλλῳ τῆς κολοκύνθης.
προσβαλόντες οὖν ἡμῖν ἀπὸ δύο πληρωμάτων ἐμάχοντο 535
καὶ πολλοὺς κατετραυμάτιζον, βάλλοντες ἀντὶ λίθων τῷ

σπέρματι τῶν κολοκυνθῶν. ἀγχωμάλως δ' ἐπιπολὺ ναυμαχοῦντες περὶ μεσημβρίαν εἴδομεν κατόπιν τῶν Κολοκυνθοπειρατῶν προσπλέοντας τοὺς Καρυοναύτας· πολέμιοι
540 δ' ἦσαν ἀλλήλοις, ὡς ἔδειξαν. ἐπειδὴ γὰρ κἀκεῖνοι ᾔσθοντο αὐτοὺς ἐπιόντας, ἡμῶν μὲν ὠλιγώρησαν τραπόμενοι δ' ἐπ' ἐκείνους ἐναυμάχουν. ἡμεῖς δ' ἐν τοσούτῳ ἐπάραντες τὴν ὀθόνην ἐφεύγομεν, ἀπολιπόντες αὐτοὺς μαχομένους· καὶ δῆλοι ἦσαν κρατήσοντες οἱ Καρυοναῦ-
545 ται, ἅτε καὶ πλείους (πέντε γὰρ εἶχον πληρώματα) καὶ ἀπὸ ἰσχυροτέρων νεῶν μαχόμενοι· τὰ γὰρ πλοῖα ἦν αὐτοῖς κελύφη, καρύων ἡμίτομα, κεκενωμένα, μέγεθος δὲ ἑκάστου ἡμιτόμου ἐς μῆκος ὀργυιαὶ πεντεκαίδεκα. ἐπεὶ δ' ἀπεκρύψαμεν αὐτούς, ἰώμεθά τε τοὺς τραυματίας καὶ
550 τολοιπὸν ἐν τοῖς ὅπλοις ὡς ἐπίπαν ἦμεν, ἀεί τινας ἐπιβουλὰς προσδεχόμενοι· οὐ μάτην. οὔπω γοῦν ἐδεδύκει ὁ ἥλιος καὶ ἀπό τινος ἐρήμης νήσου προσήλαυνον ἡμῖν ὅσον εἴκοσιν ἄνδρες ἐπὶ δελφίνων μεγάλων ὀχούμενοι, λῃσταὶ καὶ οὗτοι· καὶ οἱ δελφῖνες αὐτοὺς ἔφερον ἀσφα-
555 λῶς, καὶ ἀναπηδῶντες ἐχρεμέτιζον, ὥσπερ ἵπποι. ἐπεὶ δὲ πλησίον ἦσαν, διαστάντες οἱ μὲν ἔνθεν οἱ δὲ ἔνθεν ἔβαλλον ἡμᾶς σηπίαις ξηραῖς καὶ ὀφθαλμοῖς καρκίνων. τοξευόντων δὲ ἡμῶν καὶ ἀκοντιζόντων οὐκέτι ὑπέμειναν, ἀλλὰ τρωθέντες οἱ πολλοὶ αὐτῶν πρὸς τὴν νῆσον κατέ-
560 φυγον.

A bird's nest seven miles in circumference. Strange portents.

Περὶ δὲ τὸ μεσονύκτιον, γαλήνης οὔσης, ἐλάθομεν προσοκείλαντες Ἀλκυόνος καλιᾷ παμμεγέθει. σταδίων που ἑξήκοντα ἦν αὐτὴ τὸ περίμετρον· ἐπέπλει δὲ ἡ Ἀλκυὼν τὰ ὠὰ θάλπουσα, οὐ πολὺ μείων τῆς καλιᾶς· καὶ

δὴ ἀναπταμένη μικροῦ μὲν κατέδυσε τὴν ναῦν τῷ ἀνέμῳ 565
τῶν πτερῶν. ᾤχετο γοῦν φεύγουσα, γοεράν τινα φωνὴν προιεμένη. ἐπιβάντες δὲ ἡμεῖς, ἡμέρας ἤδη ὑποφαινούσης, ἐθεώμεθα τὴν καλιὰν, σχεδίᾳ μεγάλῃ προσ-
εοικυῖαν, ἐκ δένδρων μεγάλων συμπεφορημένην. ἐπῆν
δὲ καὶ ᾠὰ πεντακόσια, ἕκαστον αὐτῶν Χίου πίθου περι- 570
πληθέστερον. ἤδη μέντοι καὶ οἱ νεοττοὶ ἔνδοθεν ἐφαίνοντο καὶ ἔκρωζον. πελέκεσι γοῦν διακόψαντες ἓν
τῶν ᾠῶν νεοττὸν ἄπτερον ἐξεκολάψαμεν, εἴκοσι γυπῶν
ἁδρότερον. ἐπεὶ δὲ πλέοντες ἀπέσχομεν τῆς καλιᾶς
ὅσον σταδίους διακοσίους, τέρατα ἡμῖν μεγάλα καὶ θαυ- 575
μαστὰ ἐπεσήμαινεν· ὅ τε γὰρ ἐν τῇ πρύμνῃ χηνίσκος
ἄφνω ἐπτερύξατο καὶ ἀνεβόησε· καὶ ὁ κυβερνήτης
Σκίνθαρος, φαλακρὸς ἤδη ὤν, ἀνεκόμησε· καὶ τὸ πάντων
ἤδη παραδοξότατον, ὁ γὰρ ἱστὸς τῆς νεὼς ἐξεβλάστησε
καὶ κλάδους ἀνέφυσε καὶ ἐπὶ τῷ ἄκρῳ ἐκαρποφόρησεν, 580
ὁ δὲ καρπὸς ἦν σῦκα καὶ σταφυλαὶ μεγάλαι, οὔπω πέ-
πειροι. ταῦτ᾽ ἰδόντες, ὡς τὸ εἰκὸς, ἐταράχθημεν, καὶ
ηὐχόμεθα τοῖς θεοῖς ἀποτρέψαι τὸ ἀλλόκοτον τοῦ φαν-
τάσματος.

An ocean forest bars our way. Passing through it we come upon a mighty chasm, which we cross by a bridge of water.

Οὔπω δὲ πεντακοσίους σταδίους διελθόντες εἴδομεν 585
ὕλην μεγίστην καὶ λάσιον, πιτύων καὶ κυπαρίττων. καὶ
ἡμεῖς μὲν εἰκάσαμεν ἤπειρον εἶναι· τὸ δ᾽ ἦν πέλαγος
ἄβυσσον, ἀρρίζοις δένδροις καταπεφυτευμένον· εἱστήκει
δὲ τὰ δένδρα ὅμως ἀκίνητα, ὀρθὰ, καθάπερ ἐπιπλέοντα.
πλησιάσαντες δ᾽ οὖν καὶ τὸ πᾶν κατανοήσαντες ἐν 590
ἀπόρῳ εἰχόμεθα, τί χρὴ δρᾶν. οὔτε γὰρ διὰ τῶν δένδρων
πλεῖν δυνατὸν ἦν (πυκνὰ γὰρ καὶ προσεχῆ ὑπῆρχεν)

οὔτ' ἀναστρέφειν ῥᾴδιον ἐδόκει. ἐγὼ δ' ἀνελθὼν ἐπὶ τὸ μέγιστον δένδρον ἀπεσκόπουν τὰ ἐπέκεινα ὅπως ἔχοι,
595 καὶ ἑώρων ἐπὶ σταδίους μὲν πεντήκοντα ἢ ὀλίγῳ πλείους τὴν ὕλην οὖσαν· ἔπειτα δὲ αὖθις ἕτερον Ὠκεανὸν ἐκδεχόμενον. καὶ δὴ ἐδόκει ἡμῖν ἀναθεμένους τὴν ναῦν ἐπὶ τὴν κόμην τῶν δένδρων (πυκνὴ γὰρ ἦν) ὑπερβιβάσαι, εἰ δυναίμεθα, ἐς τὴν ἑτέραν θάλατταν· καὶ οὕτως ἐποιοῦμεν.
600 ἐκδήσαντες γὰρ αὐτὴν κάλῳ μεγάλῳ καὶ ἀνελθόντες ἐπὶ τὰ δένδρα μόλις ἀνιμησάμεθα. καὶ θέντες ἐπὶ τῶν κλάδων πετάσαντές τε τὰ ἱστία καθάπερ ἐν θαλάττῃ ἐπλέομεν, τοῦ ἀνέμου προωθοῦντος ἐπισυρόμενοι· ἔνθα με καὶ τὸ Ἀντιμάχου τοῦ ποιητοῦ ἔπος ἐπεισῆλθε· φησὶ
605 γάρ που κἀκεῖνος·

Τοῖσιν δ' ὑλήεντα διὰ πλόον ἐρχομένοισι.

βιασάμενοι δ' ὅμως τὴν ὕλην ἀφικόμεθα πρὸς τὸ ὕδωρ, καὶ πάλιν ὁμοίως καταθέντες τὴν ναῦν ἐπλέομεν διὰ καθαροῦ καὶ διαυγοῦς ὕδατος, ἄχρι δὴ ἐπέστημεν χάσ-
610 ματι μεγάλῳ, ἐκ τοῦ ὕδατος διεστῶτος γεγενημένῳ, καθάπερ ἐν τῇ γῇ πολλάκις ὁρῶμεν ὑπὸ σεισμῶν γιγνόμενα διαχωρίσματα. ἡ μὲν οὖν ναῦς, καθελόντων ἡμῶν τὰ ἱστία, οὐ ῥᾳδίως ἔστη, παρ' ὀλίγον ἐλθοῦσα κατενεχθῆναι. ὑπερκύψαντες δὲ ἡμεῖς ἑωρῶμεν βάθος ὅσον
615 σταδίων χιλίων, μάλα φοβερὸν καὶ παράδοξον· εἱστήκει γὰρ τὸ ὕδωρ ὥσπερ μεμερισμένον· περιβλέποντες δὲ ὁρῶμεν κατὰ δεξιὰν οὐ πάνυ πόρρωθεν γέφυραν ἐπεζευγμένην ὕδατος συνάπτοντος τὰ πελάγη κατὰ τὴν ἐπιφάνειαν, κἀκ τῆς ἑτέρας θαλάττης ἐς τὴν ἑτέραν
620 διαρρέοντος. προσελάσαντες οὖν ταῖς κώπαις κατ' ἐκεῖνο παρεδράμομεν, καὶ μετὰ πολλῆς ἀγωνίας ἐπεράσαμεν οὔποτε προσδοκήσαντες.

Combat with the Ox-headed islanders. More strange sights.

Τοὐντεῦθεν ἡμᾶς ὑπεδέχετο πέλαγός τε προσηνὲς καὶ νῆσος οὐ μεγάλη, εὐπροσίτως συνοικουμένη· ἐνέμοντο δὲ αὐτὴν ἄνθρωποι ἄγριοι Βουκέφαλοι, κέρατα ἔχοντες, οἷον 625 παρ' ἡμῖν τὸν Μινώταυρον ἀναπλάττουσιν. ἀποβάντες δὲ προσῄειμεν ὑδρευσόμενοι καὶ σιτία ληψόμενοι, εἴποθεν δυνηθείημεν· οὐκ ἔτι γὰρ εἴχομεν· καὶ ὕδωρ μὲν αὐτοῦ πλησίον εὕρομεν, ἄλλο δὲ οὐδὲν ἐνεφαίνετο, πλὴν μυκηθμὸς πολὺς οὐ πόρρωθεν ἠκούετο· δόξαντες οὖν 630 ἀγέλην εἶναι βοῶν κατ' ὀλίγον προχωροῦντες ἐπέστημεν τοῖς ἀνθρώποις. οἱ δὲ ἰδόντες ἡμᾶς ἐδίωκον, καὶ τρεῖς μὲν τῶν ἑταίρων λαμβάνουσιν· οἱ δὲ λοιποὶ πρὸς τὴν θάλατταν κατεφεύγομεν. εἶτα μέντοι πάντες ὁπλισάμενοι (οὐ γὰρ ἐδόκει ἡμῖν ἀτιμωρήτους περιϊδεῖν τοὺς 635 φίλους) ἐμπίπτομεν τοῖς Βουκεφάλοις τὰ κρέα τῶν ἀνῃρημένων διαιρουμένοις· βοήσαντες δὲ πάντες ἐδιώκομεν, καὶ κτείνομέν γε ὅσον πεντήκοντα καὶ ζῶντας αὐτῶν δύο λαμβάνομεν, καὶ αὖθις ὀπίσω ἀνεστρέφομεν τοὺς αἰχμαλώτους ἔχοντες· σιτίον μέντοι οὐδὲν εὕρομεν. 640 οἱ μὲν οὖν ἄλλοι παρῄνουν ἀποσφάττειν τοὺς εἰλημμένους· ἐγὼ δὲ οὐκ ἐδοκίμαζον, ἀλλὰ δήσας ἐφύλαττον αὐτούς, ἄχρι δὴ ἀφίκοντο παρὰ τῶν Βουκεφάλων πρέσβεις ἀπαιτοῦντες ἐπὶ λύτροις τοὺς συνειλημμένους· συνίεμεν γὰρ αὐτῶν διανευόντων καὶ γοερόν τι μυκωμένων, ὥσπερ 645 ἱκετευόντων. τὰ λύτρα δ' ἦν τυροὶ πολλοὶ καὶ ἰχθῦς ξηροὶ καὶ κρόμμυα καὶ ἔλαφοι τέτταρες, τρεῖς ἑκάστη πόδας ἔχουσα, δύο μὲν τοὺς ὄπισθεν οἱ δὲ πρόσω ἐς ἕνα συμπεφύκεσαν. ἐπὶ τούτοις ἀποδόντες τοὺς συνειλημμένους καὶ μίαν ἡμέραν ἐπιμείναντες ἀνήχθημεν. ἤδη 650 δὲ ἰχθύες τε ἡμῖν ἐφαίνοντο καὶ ὄρνεα παρεπέτετο καὶ

ἄλλα, ὁπόσα γῆς πλησίον οὔσης σημεῖα, προὐφαίνετο. μετ' ὀλίγον δὲ καὶ ἄνδρας εἴδομεν καινῷ τρόπῳ ναυτιλίας χρωμένους· αὐτοὶ γὰρ καὶ ναῦται καὶ νῆες ἦσαν. ἄλλοι
655 δὲ μετὰ τούτους, ἐπὶ φελλῶν καθήμενοι, ζεύξαντες δύο δελφῖνας, ἤλαυνόν τε καὶ ἡνιόχευον· οἱ δὲ προϊόντες ἐπεσύροντο τοὺς φελλούς. οὗτοι ἡμᾶς οὔτε ἠδίκουν οὔτε ἔφευγον, ἀλλ' ἤλαυνον ἀδεῶς τε καὶ εἰρηνικῶς, τὸ εἶδος τοῦ ἡμετέρου πλοίου θαυμάζοντες καὶ πάντοθεν περισκο-
660 ποῦντες.

Our adventures with the donkey-legged women. Conclusion of our voyage.

Ἑσπέρας δὲ ἤδη προσήχθημεν νήσῳ οὐ μεγάλῃ· κατῴκητο δὲ αὕτη ὑπὸ γυναικῶν, ὡς ἐνομίζομεν, Ἑλλάδα φωνὴν προϊεμένων· προσῄεσαν γὰρ καὶ ἐδεξιοῦντο καὶ ἠσπάζοντο, καλαὶ πᾶσαι καὶ νεανίδες, ποδήρεις τοὺς
665 χιτῶνας ἐπισυρόμεναι. ἡ μὲν οὖν νῆσος ἐκαλεῖτο Καβαλοῦσα· ἡ δὲ πόλις Ὑδαμαρδία. λαβοῦσαι δ' οὖν ἡμᾶς αἱ γυναῖκες ἑκάστη πρὸς ἑαυτὴν ἀπῆγε καὶ ξένον ἐποιεῖτο. ἐγὼ δὲ μικρὸν ὑποστὰς (οὐ γὰρ χρηστὰ ἐμαντευόμην) ἀκριβέστερόν τε περιβλέπων ὁρῶ πολλῶν ἀνθρώπων
670 ὀστᾶ καὶ κρανία κείμενα· καὶ τὸ μὲν βοὴν ἱστάναι καὶ τοὺς ἑταίρους συγκαλεῖν καὶ ἐς τὰ ὅπλα χωρεῖν οὐκ ἐδοκίμαζον· προχειρισάμενος δὲ τὴν μαλάχην πολλὰ ηὐχόμην αὐτῇ διαφυγεῖν ἐκ τῶν παρόντων κακῶν. μετ' ὀλίγον δέ, τῆς ξένης διακονουμένης, εἶδον τὰ σκέλη οὐ
675 γυναικὸς ἀλλ' ὄνου ὁπλάς· καὶ δὴ σπασάμενος τὸ ξίφος συλλαμβάνω τε αὐτὴν καὶ δήσας περὶ τῶν ὅλων ἀνέκρινον· ἡ δὲ ἄκουσα μὲν εἶπε δὲ ὅμως, αὐτὰς μὲν εἶναι θαλασσίους γυναῖκας, Ὀνοσκελέας προσαγορευομένας τροφὴν δὲ ποιεῖσθαι τοὺς ἐπιδημοῦντας ξένους. "Ἐπει-

δὰν γάρ," ἔφη, "μεθύσωμεν αὐτοὺς, κοιμωμένοις ἐπιχειροῦ- 680
μεν." ἀκούσας δὲ ταῦτα ἐκείνην μὲν κατέλιπον αὐτοῦ
δεδεμένην, αὐτὸς δὲ ἀνελθὼν ἐπὶ τὸ στέγος ἐβόων τε καὶ
τοὺς ἑταίρους συνεκάλουν. ἐπεὶ δὲ συνῆλθον, τὰ πάντα
ἐμήνυον αὐτοῖς, καὶ τά τε ὀστᾶ ἐδείκνυον καὶ ἦγον εἴσω
πρὸς τὴν δεδεμένην· ἡ δὲ αὐτίκα ὕδωρ ἐγένετο καὶ 685
ἀφανὴς ἦν. ὅμως δὲ τὸ ξίφος εἰς τὸ ὕδωρ καθῆκα
πειρώμενος· τὸ δὲ αἷμα ἐγένετο. ταχέως οὖν ἐπὶ ναῦν
κατελθόντες ἀπεπλεύσαμεν· καὶ ἐπεὶ ἡμέρα ὑπηύγαζε,
τὴν ἤπειρον ἀποβλεπόμενοι εἰκάζομεν εἶναι τὴν ἀντιπέραν τῇ ὑφ' ἡμῶν οἰκουμένῃ κειμένην. προσκυνήσαντες 690
δ' οὖν καὶ προσευξάμενοι περὶ τῶν μελλόντων ἐσκοποῦ-
μεν, καὶ τοῖς μὲν ἐδόκει ἐπιβᾶσι μόνον αὖθις ὀπίσω
ἀναστρέφειν· τοῖς δὲ τὸ μὲν πλοῖον αὐτοῦ καταλιπεῖν,
ἀνελθόντας δὲ εἰς τὴν μεσόγαιαν πειραθῆναι τῶν ἐνοικ-
ούντων. ἐν ὅσῳ δὲ ταῦτα ἐλογιζόμεθα, χειμὼν σφοδρὸς 695
ἐπιπεσὼν καὶ προσαράξας τὸ σκάφος τῷ αἰγιαλῷ διέλυ-
σεν. ἡμεῖς δὲ μόλις ἐξενηξάμεθα, τὰ ὅπλα ἕκαστος καὶ
εἴ τι ἄλλο οἷός τε ἦν ἁρπασάμενοι.

Ταῦτα μὲν οὖν τὰ μέχρι τῆς ἑτέρας γῆς συνενεχθέντα
μοι ἐν τῇ θαλάττῃ καὶ παρὰ τὸν πλοῦν ἐν ταῖς νήσοις 700
καὶ ἐν τῷ ἀέρι καὶ μετὰ ταῦτα ἐν τῷ κήτει, καὶ ἐπεὶ
ἐξήλθομεν παρά τε τοῖς ἥρωσι καὶ τοῖς ὀνείροις, καὶ τὰ
τελευταῖα παρὰ τοῖς Βουκεφάλοις καὶ ταῖς Ὀνοσκελέαις
τὰ δ' ἐπὶ τῆς γῆς ἐν ταῖς ἑξῆς βίβλοις διηγήσομαι.

NOTES.

BOOK I.

Line 1. ἀθλητικοῖς, usually neuter, from *τὰ ἀθλητικά*, but here = *ἀθληταῖς*. So in next line ἠσκημένοις is the middle voice, 'those who practise,' etc., answering to *ἐσπουδακόσιν* in l. 6.

l. 4. μέρος γοῦν, etc., a parenthesis, '*at least* they suppose.' *Γοῦν* (*γε οὖν*) explains the former statement by giving a reason for it; i.e. the athletes provide for relaxation *because* they think it important.

l. 7. σπουδαιοτέρων, Lat. *seria*, as in Virg. *Ecl.* vii. 17:—

'Posthabui tamen illorum mea *seria* ludo.'

l. 10. ἃ μὴ, etc., '*such as* will not,' etc. = *οἷα μὴ* after *τοιούτοις*. Here *μὴ* is properly used instead of *οὐ*, but Lucian often does not observe the distinction. See l. 24, n; also l. 503; ii. l. 453.

l. 11. ψιλὴν, etc., 'a bare enticement to the mind,' etc., i.e. which not only amuses by a narrative of marvellous adventures, but engages the literary or critical faculty by imitating the accounts of professed poets and historians.

l. 18. οὐκ ἀκωμῳδήτως, 'not without a spice of comedy' or 'satire.'

ᾔνικται, 'contains some tacit allusion.' See *αἰνίσσομαι* in Lexicon.

l. 21. σοι, i.e. to the reader, whoever he may be. The *Vera Historia* is not addressed to any one in particular; but Lucian may have intended it for his friend Philo, to whom a previous treatise *On the Art of Writing History* had been dedicated.

l. 22. Fragments of Ctesias' History of India are preserved in the Bibliotheca of Photius. Many of the wonders he relates are distortions of fact, e.g. the 'talking-birds,' and the black dog-headed men, with long teeth and nails, who have a voice like a bark and make gestures and grimaces.

l. 24. μήτε, etc. We should rather expect *οὔτε*, as expressing a simple fact. But the free use of *μὴ* for *οὐ*, especially with participles (as in l. 51) is a characteristic of Lucian's style. Cp. l. 503, n.; ii. l. 453. Clyde, *Greek Syntax*, 648, Obs. 2, attributes the prevalence of *μὴ* to the progress of refinement in later times, *μὴ* being a less downright and therefore politer form of negation.

l. 25. Nothing is left of the works of Iambulus. Vossius gives the title of a treatise *De mirificis hominum formis*, but does not mention the one alluded to in the text. Diodorus Siculus is supposed to have copied from Iambulus in his description of India.

ll. 26, 27. Observe the position of the articles **τὸ** and **τὴν**,—'*though* the falsity of his fictions is manifest, *still* the design of the composition is not unpleasing.'

l. 28. **ἄλλοι**, especially Herodotus, to whom Lucian evidently alludes in several places, sometimes by name, as in ii. 87, 438.

l. 29. **ὡς δή**, ironical, '*professing* to relate their own adventures,' etc.

l. 30. **ἱστοροῦντες**, in its later sense of 'narrating,' whence our 'history.' Cp. the title of this work, Ἀληθὴς Ἱστορία. Originally the word meant 'enquiry,' or 'research;' thus Herodotus calls his book Ἱστορίαι. The proper term for 'history' was *συγγραφή* (cp. ll. 13, 19, 28), which is applied to the work of Thucydides, Θουκυδίδης Ἀθηναῖος ξυνέγραψε, Thuc. i. 1.

l. 31. **βίων καινότητας**, 'strange modes of life.' Καινὸς especially denotes what is new and strange (hence *καινὰ* = 'innovations,' *καινοὶ θεοί*, 'strange gods'); *νέος* is simply 'new' in point of time.

l. 32. **βωμολοχίας**, 'buffoonery.' See *βωμόλοχος* in Lexicon.

l. 33. The tales of Odysseus at the court of Alcinous, about the Cyclops, the bag in which the winds were confined, the enchantments of Circe, etc., are related in Books ix—xii. of the Odyssey.

l. 37. **ἰδιώτας**, 'simple-minded.' This secondary sense of *ἰδιώτης* (whence came that of 'idiot') appears in Xen. *Memorabilia*, iii. 12, and must have been common before Lucian's time. For a similar estimate of the Phaeacians, cp. Juvenal, *Sat.* xv. 23:—

'Tum *vacui capitis* populum Phaeaca putavit.'

l. 40. **φιλοσοφεῖν**, in allusion to Plato's myths, especially the one that concludes the *Republic*.

l. 41. **εἰ**, 'whether,' instead of *ὅτι* after *ἐθαύμασα*, implying that he can hardly believe it to be a fact. Cp. Mark xv. 44, *ἐθαύμασεν εἰ ἤδη τέθνηκεν*.

l. 46. **εὐγνωμονέστερον**, 'with a more honest intention.'

l. 47. **κἂν** = *καὶ ἂν*, but *ἂν* is rare with the fut. ind. When it does occur, it makes an assertion qualified by an understood condition,—'I will e'en (if you will allow me) state this one true fact,' or something of the kind. Cp. Plato, *Rep.* Bk. x. ch. 13, *οὐχ ἥκει, οὐδ' ἂν ἥξει*, 'nor is he *likely* to come.' This naive avowal made at the outset rather spoils the effect of the story; it might perhaps have come better at the end.

l. 50. **μήτε** for *οὔτε*. Cp. l. 24, n.

l. 51. **τὴν ἀρχὴν**, (usually *ἀρχὴν* in this sense) = *omnino*, 'at all,' or 'which could never possibly have happened.'

ll. 54, 55. The Pillars of Hercules were Mount Abyla in Mauritania, and Calpe in Spain, one on either side of the Fretum Gaditanum, now the Straits of Gibraltar. According to the legend they were once a continuous mountain, which Hercules rent asunder. Outside these Straits lay the Western Ocean, a tract almost unknown, except possibly to some bolder Phoenician adventurers. The term *Oceanus* was originally applied to the fabled river (the ὠκεάνοιο ῥέεθρα of Homer) which was believed to encircle the world; but as geographical knowledge advanced it was used to designate the great outside expanse of waters, especially the Atlantic, as distinguished from the Mediterranean or inner sea. Béquet, a French translator of the *Vera Historia*, observes that if Lucian had really made the voyage he describes, he might have discovered America (οἱ πέραν κατοικοῦντες, l. 59). See note on ii. 384.

l. 57. **περιεργία**, 'curiosity,' lit. 'over-carefulness,' from περὶ, denoting excess, as in περικαλλής, etc. Cp. Acts xix. 19.

l. 65. **ἄκατος**, a light craft or 'pinnace.' Lucian's exactitude, giving such an air of reality to this 'lie with a circumstance,' is very amusing.

l. 69. **ἐπεδίδου**, 'began to freshen.' Ἐπιδιδόναι = 'to increase,' ἐπὶ signifying addition. Cp. our expression 'to put it *on*' in rowing.

l. 72. **αὑτοὺς** (= ἑαυτοὺς) for ἡμᾶς αὐτούς. This use of the 3rd reflexive pronoun for the 1st or 2nd is not uncommon. Cp. Plato, *Phædo*, δεῖ ἡμᾶς ἀνερέσθαι ἑαυτούς: 1 John i. 8, ἑαυτοὺς πλανῶμεν, 'we deceive *ourselves*.'

l. 75. **οὐ τραχεῖ**, etc., 'surrounded by the noise of no roughening wave,' i.e. 'around which the waves beat no longer furiously,' *quam non turbato circumsonat aequore fluctus*. The passive περιηχεῖσθαι may be compared with such expressions as αὐλούμενος, 'having the flute played to one,' i.e. 'hearing the flute' (Xen. *Anab.* vi. 1. 11), etc. Cp. Ovid, *Trist.* iii. 13, 47, 'Scythio *circumsonor* ore' = 'I hear the Scythian speech all around me.' The position of the article between the adjective and noun makes τραχεῖ predicative.

l. 76. **ὡς ἂν**, i.e. 'as you *might expect*.' Ἂν often stands thus alone, when the context can be easily supplied, especially in the phrases ὡς ἄν, ὥσπερ ἄν, ὥσπερ ἂν εἰ (= *quasi*), as in Plato, *Gorgias*, φοβούμενος ὥσπερ ἂν εἰ παῖς, i.e. 'as a child would be afraid.' Cp. ii. 490.

l. 87. **ἐμοὶ δοκεῖν**, 'in my opinion.' The infin. without ὡς is common in short colloquial phrases, as ὀλίγου δεῖν, 'almost,' πολλοῦ δεῖν, 'far from it,' etc.

l. 90. **καὶ** = ὅτε, 'when,' after οὔπω, implying that the two things happened continuously. Cp. Mark xv. 25, ἦν ὥρα τρίτη, καὶ ἐσταύρωσαν αὐτόν.

l. 91. The double superlative is rare. Cp. Soph. *Phil.* 631, πλεῖστον *ἔχθιστος*: Plato, *Timaeus*, ch. 44, *τῶν μάλιστα ἀνοητοτάτων*. Here it adds force to the burlesque description, 'for all the world exactly like our Chian wine.'

l. 92. **ἐνιαχοῦ** = *ἐνιαχῇ*, 'in some parts.'

l. 93. **ἐπῄει**, 'it occurred to us' (lit. 'entered our minds'), or 'we were induced.

l. 95. **δόξαν**, the accusative of the participle used 'absolutely,' but really an accus. of respect, lit. 'it having seemed good to me.' So *ἐξὸν*, *παρὸν*, *τυχὸν*, etc.

l. 99. **ἀφ' ὧν**, sc. *σταγόνων*, the preceding *ἑκάστης* being virtually equivalent to *πασῶν*.

l. 103. **ἀμέλει**, = 'to be sure,' 'of course,'—properly the imperative of *ἀμελέω*, = 'never mind,'—i.e. 'don't trouble yourself.' In the *Clouds* of Aristophanes, Socrates asks Strepsiades, *πῶς οὖν δυνήσει μανθάνειν*; to which he replies, *ἀμέλει, καλῶς*, 'very well, of course.' It is very common in the *Characters* of Theophrastus.

l. 105. **ἐκεράννυμεν**, etc., 'we tempered' or 'took off the excessive strength of the liquor.' Wine was mixed with water in the *κρατὴρ* before drinking. **Οἰνοφαγίας** instead of *οἰνοποσίας*, because the wine was taken in a solid form.

l. 107. **χρῆμα**. Cp. Hdt. i. 36, *συὸς μέγα χρῆμα*, 'a huge monster of a boar,' Aristoph. *Nubes*, 2, *χρῆμα τῶν νυκτῶν ὅσον*, *Acharn.* 150, *ὅσον τὸ χρῆμα παρνόπων*.

l. 111. For the story of Daphne's transformation into a laurel-tree, see Ovid, *Met.* i. 452–567.

l. 116. **Λύδιον**, usually *Λυδίαν* in feminine. Derivative adjectives in *-ιος* commonly have only two terminations, but they vary considerably.

l. 119. Cp. Eur. *Hec.* 1050, *τυφλὸν τυφλῷ στείχοντα* **παραφόρῳ** *ποδί*.

l. 120. An evident allusion to Virgil's story of Polydorus and the groaning cornel-tree in *Aeneid* iii. 22–46.

l. 142. **τὴν καθ' ἡμᾶς οἰκουμένην**, = 'our world,' lit. 'according to,' or 'with respect to us.' Hence *κατὰ* with accus. became almost equivalent to a possessive pronoun, as frequently in the N. T., e.g. Acts xviii. 28, *τῶν καθ' ὑμᾶς ποιητῶν*, 'your own poets,' xviii. 15, *νόμου τοῦ καθ' ὑμᾶς*, 'your law,' etc.

l. 152. **εὑρεθείη**. The opt. denotes frequency, 'whenever one was found,' Lat. *si quando reperiretur*. But **προστέτακται**, the perf. ind., implies that it was a standing order.

καὶ δὴ, 'accordingly.' The *δὴ* particularises *ἡμᾶς* with reference to the general statement *εἴ τις . . ξένος*, and the second *καὶ* emphasises *ἡμᾶς*—'*us* too, in accordance with their instructions, they took,' etc.

l. 157. **καὶ ὃς**, a remnant of the old demonstrative use of *ὅς*. Originally *ὁ* and *ὃς* were used indiscriminately both ways; thus in Homer *τά*,

τοὺς, etc. = *quae*, *quos*, etc., and **ὃς** = *is*, as in *μηδ' ὃς φύγοι*, *Il.* vi. 59. Afterwards there remained only the phrases *καὶ ὅς. ἦ δ' ὅς* = 'quoth he,' *ὃς μὲν . . . ὃς δὲ* in Demosthenes, and the rare *ὃς καὶ ὅς* = 'this or that man,' Hdt. iv. 68. (Jelf, *Gr. Gram.* § 816.)

l. 158. The story of Endymion, beloved and visited by the Moon on Latmos, is the subject of the 11th Dialogue of the Gods, between Aphrodite and Selene.

l. 163. **δεόμεθα**, the ind. for the opt. in a dependent clause after a verb in the past tense. But a Greek writer, to throw life into his narrative, often uses the same tense and mood in a reported speech which the original speaker would have used, altering only the person (as *δεῖσθε* into *δεόμεθα*). Cp. Hdt. vi. 132, *φὰς ἐπὶ χώρην τινὰ ἄξειν, ὅθεν χρυσὸν* **οἴσονται**, = 'whence they *would* get,' where the speaker would have said *οἴσεσθε*.

l. 176. **Ἱππομυρμήκων**, 'Horse-ants,' or 'Ant-cavalry.'

l. 180. **γῦπας**, etc. This is an instance of Lucian's art in making impossibilities seem natural. The new-comers undertake the management of their vulture-steeds at a day's notice, as quite an ordinary affair.

l. 186. **ἐγένοντο**, because of the plural *notion* implied in *τὸ πλῆθος*. Cp. l. 220, Thuc. i. 20, *τὸ πλῆθος* **οἴονται**.

l. 190. **λαχανοπτέρων**, 'cabbage-fowl.' This and some other renderings of these strange names are taken from Tooke's translation of 1820. But the student may exercise his own ingenuity.

l. 193. **Κεγχροβόλοι**, 'Millet-shooters.' The term **Σκοροδομάχοι** may either refer to their being primed, like fighting-cocks, with garlic (whence the verb *σκοροδίζειν* in Aristophanes), or to their throwing garlic amongst the enemy, the stink of which would be intolerable.

ἐτετάχατο. This Ionic form for *τεταγμένοι ἦσαν* was sometimes used in Attic Greek. Cp. *ἐφθάραται* for *ἐφθαρμένοι εἰσὶ*, Thuc. iii. 13, *ἀντιτετάχαται*, Xen. *Anab.* iv. 8. 5.

l. 204. **ὑπὲρ τὴν Καππαδοκίαν**, probably because Cappadocia was famous for its breed of horses. Lucian would know it well, as it bordered on his native district of Commagene. See Map of Asia Minor.

l. 212. **φολιδωτοί**, 'plated with scales,' like crocodiles. In Xen. *Cyropaedia*, vi. 4, 2, we have *χιτὼν φολιδωτός*, a variant reading for *στολιδωτός*.

θέρμινοι, 'made of lupines,' the derivative adj. of *θέρμος*. [Distinguish *θέρμος*, 'lupine,' from *θερμός*, 'hot.']

l. 219. **ὡς ἕκαστοι** probably means 'each in his order,' = *ἐν τάξει*. What follows is a good parody on actual descriptions, such as that of the battle of Cunaxa in Xen. *Anab.* i. 8, 10, or the one in the *Cyropaedia*, vii. 1.

l. 220. **τὸ πεζὸν ἦσαν.** Cp. l. 186 n.

l. 223. **προσέταξε**, sc. *ὁ βασιλεὺς*, i.e. Phaethon.

l. 226. **Νυκτερίων**, etc., 'Nightbird, the son of Fairweather.'

l. 231. **ἀλλὰ καὶ αὐτοί**, etc., perhaps in allusion to the story in Herodotus, v. 111, of the horse of Artybius, which was trained to stand on its hind legs and fight with a man.

l. 234. **Ἀεροκώνωπες**, 'Gnat-riders.'

l. 236. **Ἀεροκόρακες**, 'Air-crows.' But as all crows are such, it may be better to read *Ἀεροκάρδακες*, i.e. 'Air-mercenaries.'

l. 237. **πλὴν**, 'except that,' or 'nevertheless,'=*πλὴν ὅτι* or *ἀλλά*. Cp. ii. 629; Xen. *Anab.* iii. 2, 26, *πλὴν Ἀπολλωνίδης τις ἦν.*

l. 241. **μαλάχης ἰῷ.** The joke lies in the fact that mallow is really a *healing* plant.

l. 242. **Καυλομύκητες**, 'Stalky-mushrooms.'

l. 245. **Κυνοβάλανοι**, 'Dog-acorns,' or 'Acorn-dogs.'

l. 249. **τῶν συμμάχων**, the partitive gen., 'some of those auxiliaries, etc. . . . besides the Cloud-centaurs.'

Γαλαξίου, gen. of **Γαλαξίας**, 'the Milky Way.'

l. 252. **μήποτε ὤφελον**, =*ὤφελον μήποτε ἀφικέσθαι*, which accounts for the *μή*, since *ὤφελον* literally means 'they ought,' i.e. 'would that they,' etc. So the Latin *debere*, as in Ovid, *Her.* xii. 4:—

'*Debuerant* fusos evoluisse suos.'

Cp. Hom. *Il.* ix. 698, *μηδ' ὄφελες λίσσεσθαι*, Soph. *Philoct.* 969, *μήποτ' ὤφελον λιπεῖν.*

l. 270. **μὴ ἄρα**, etc., 'whether Homer might not have supposed,' etc. Μή in indirect questions or suppositions with the indicative implies that the case probably is so, with the subjunctive or optative greater doubt or suspicion is suggested.

l. 272. For the death of Sarpedon, king of Lycia, whom Patroclus slew, see *Iliad*, xvi. 459, etc. *αἱματοέσσας δὲ ψιάδας κατέχευεν ἔραζε, Παῖδα φίλον τιμῶν.*

l. 280. The Colossus of Rhodes was more than 100 feet high. *Ἐξ ἡμισείας* means the half figure of the man above the horse's back.

l. 303. **περιορᾶν**, 'to overlook,' i.e. 'to allow' anything to happen. Herodotus uses the phrase frequently, e.g. iv. 118, *μὴ περιΐδητε ἡμέας διαφθαρέντας.* Cp. ii. 635.

l. 307. **γενομένης δὶς ἐκκλησίας**, etc., possibly in allusion to the reversal by the Athenians of their cruel decree against the Mitylenaeans after the revolt of that town (Thuc. iii. 36). Aristophanes, *Acharnians*, 630, 632, bestows upon his countrymen the epithets *ταχύβουλοι* and *μετάβουλοι.*

l. 311. **ἐπὶ τῷ**, 'on condition that.' So *ἐπὶ τούτοις*, 'on these terms,' *ἐφ' οἷς*, *ἐφ' ᾧτε*, etc.

l. 312. **τὸ διατείχισμα**, 'the partition wall.'

ll. 324, 325. The names of the Sun's representatives may be rendered 'Firebrace,' 'Summerheat,' and 'Flamington;' those of the Moon 'Nightlove,' 'Moonson,' and 'Flashlight' (or 'All-a-blaze').

l. 340. Herodotus, iv. 75, says that the Scythians were wont to regale themselves by a peculiar mode of intoxication, produced by inhaling the fumes of hemp-seed.

ἀναθυμιώμενον, 'rising in fumes.' See *θυμιάω* in Lexicon.

l. 343. **ὑγρὸν ἀνιείς**, 'producing a liquid.' *Ὑγρὸν* is a substantive here.

l. 349. **μονοδάκτυλοι** probably refers to the feet, as well as to the hands.

l. 350. **ἀπομύττονται**, 'discharge from their nostrils;' *emungunt*.

l. 359. **ὥσπερ πήρᾳ**, etc. Truth is sometimes at least as strange as fiction; for the kangaroo, opossum, and other animals of the order Marsupialia have just such a pouch or false stomach as is here described, in which their young grow and are nourished up to a certain age. These animals are found only in America and Australia, and therefore could not have been known to Lucian.

l. 370. **περιαιρετούς**, 'removable' at pleasure. Thucydides, ii. 13, describes the gold with which the statue of Athenè in the Parthenon was overlaid as *ἅπαν περιαιρετόν*. In *Household Words*, June 1850, there is a story entitled 'My Wonderful Adventures in Skitzland,' where the inhabitants could take themselves to pieces, and a certain Baron sends his eyes by coach to pay a visit.

l. 373. **χρησάμενοι** (middle), 'borrowing.' Cp. the line in the Anthologia, of a blind man carrying a lame one, *πόδας χρήσας, ὄμματα χρησάμενος*, '*lending* feet and *borrowing* eyes.'

l. 377. **διαλυόμενος**, etc., possibly in allusion to the theory of Empedocles, which represented birth as a 'mingling' of elements, and death as a 'separation of the mingled' (*μῖξίς τε διάλλαξίς τε μιγέντων*).

l. 385. Here **μή** is rightly used with the indefinite pronoun *ὅστις*. Cp. l. 10, n.

l. 391. **ἐν τῷ κήτει**. Lucian here anticipates another adventure, the account of which begins at l. 445.

θερμίνην. Cp. l. 212, n.

l. 406. **Λυχνόπολιν**, perhaps suggested by the account in Herodotus, ii. 62, of the Feast of Lanterns at Sais in Egypt. From Lucian Rabelais may have borrowed his description of Lantern-land, with its port of the Lychnobii and the Lantern-guides.

l. 430. **Νεφελοκοκκυγίαν** is the name Aristophanes gives to the airy cloud-built town in his comedy of the *Birds*. Lucian affects to believe that the poet intended it for a reality (l. 434).

l. 432. **Κορωνὸς**, a masculine form of *κορωνή*, a crow.

Κοττυφίων is formed from *κόττυφος* (*κόσσυφος*), a blackbird.

l. 439. **ἐνδιδόντος**, 'subsiding' (as we say, 'to give in'). Cp. its opposite *ἐπιδιδόναι*, l. 69 and note.

l. 456. **οὐκ ἔφθη συναράξαι**, lit. 'he was not quick enough to crush us,' i.e. 'he just missed crushing us.' *Φθάνειν* with a participle, 'to do a thing quickly' or 'beforehand' is common enough; it is rarely constructed with the infinitive. Cp. Aristoph. *Nubes*, 1384, *οὐκ ἔφθης φράσαι.*

l. 457. **ἀραιωμάτων**, 'the gaps,' through the verb *ἀραιόω* from *ἀραιὸς*, 'thin;' hence 'porous,' or 'full of holes.'

l. 464. **ἐμοὶ δοκεῖν.** Cp. l. 87, n.

l. 467. **ἐξειργασμένοις**, 'tilled land.' Cp. Hdt. v. 29, *ἀγροὶ εὖ ἐξεργασμένοι.*

l. 469. **δένδρων.** Gulls and kingfishers do *not* build in trees.

l. 471. **ἀναστήσας . . . ὑπεστηρίξαμεν** instead of *ἐμοῦ ἀναστήσαντος*, etc., because the *ἐγὼ* in apposition with *ἀναστήσας* is included in the subject of the plural verb;—'after *I* had roused my comrades, *we* underpropped our ship.'

l. 476. **ἀναχάνοι.** For this force of the optative, cp. l. 152, n.

l. 493. **ἐναλίων δαιμόνων.** Cp. Eur. *Iph. in Tauris*, 267, where the herdsmen espying Pylades and Orestes on the rock exclaim—*δαίμονές τινες θάσσουσιν οἵδε*, and 372—

εἴτ' οὖν ἐπ' ἀκταῖς θάσσετον Διοσκόρω, etc.

l. 503. **μὴ** would regularly be *οὐ*, as stating a fact after *ὅτι*. Cp. l. 24, n.

l. 508. **ἐπεποίητο**, etc., middle pluperfects, 'had made (for himself),' etc. The so-called perfect passive also serves for the perfect middle, especially in deponent verbs and verbs whose active and middle voices differ in meaning.

l. 511. **ἐπεπόνθειμεν.** This in pure Attic style should rather be *ἐπάθομεν*. The Greeks commonly used the aorist in relative or dependent clauses, when we use the pluperfect, as *ᾐτιᾶτο αὐτὸν ὅτι οὐκ ἦλθεν*, 'because he *had* not come.' Lucian's frequent use of pluperfects is a mark of his later style.

l. 512. **νήσῳ**, the wine island, l. 74, etc.

l. 538. **τῆς καταπόσεως**, 'since we were swallowed up.' The genitive (usually with *ἐκ* or *ἀπὸ*) marks the point of time *from* which the period is reckoned.

l. 542. **ἄμικτοι**, 'unsociable.' In Soph. *Trach.* 1095, the Centaurs are called *ἄμικτον ἱπποβάμονα στρατόν*.

l. 543. **μὲν οὖν** = *immo*, 'nay,' or 'nay, rather.' In replies *μὲν οὖν* has a sort of *corrective* force, stating the fact more precisely; so here *πολλοὶ* corrects the *τινὲς* of the question.

l. 545. **Ταριχᾶνες**, 'Bloatermen,' from *τάριχος*, salt or dried fish.

l. 546. **ἐγχελυωπὸν**, 'with eel's eyes' (*ἔγχελυς*).

l. 548. **Τριτωνομένδητες**, perhaps 'Mermen-stoats,' from the description in the next line.

l. 550. **Καρκινόχειρες**, 'Crab-fists.'

ll. 552, 553. **Παγουρίδαι**, 'Shell-tails,' from *πάγουρος*.

Ψηττόποδες, 'Flounder-footed.'

l. 568. **ἡ οὐκ ἀπόδοσις**, 'the non-payment.' Cp. Thuc. i. 137, *τὴν τῶν γεφυρῶν οὐ διάλυσιν*: iii. 95, *τὴν οὐ περιτείχισιν*. In these instances *οὐ* states the fact, but *ἡ μὴ ἐμπειρία*, Aristoph. *Eccles.* 115, =' *if* one has no experience.'

προθεσμίας, sc. *ἡμέρας*, 'appointed day.' Cp. ii. 141. At Athens *προθεσμία* was a legal term for the period within which actions for debt or damage must be brought.

l. 576. **ἐπειδὰν ἴδωσι**, instead of the regular construction *ἐπεὶ ἴδοιεν*, in a dependent clause after a verb in the past tense (*προείρητο*). The principle of this construction is explained in the note on *δεόμεθα*, l. 163.

l. 586. **τῇ μάχῃ**, 'the battle-field.' Cp. *μέχρι τῆς μάχης*, Xen. *Anab.* ii. 2. 6.

l. 590. **Πήλαμος**, probably a variation from *πηλαμὺς*, a kind of tunny-fish.

l. 617. **ἐνδοτέρω**, from *ἔνδον*. Primitive adverbs (i.e. those not derived from adjectives), form their comparative and superlative in *-ω*, as *ἀνωτέρω*, *ἀνωτάτω*, etc. But some have the additional forms in *-τερον* and *-τατα*, as *ἐγγύτερον*, *ἐγγύτατα*.

l. 626. **αὐτοκλάδοις καὶ αὐτοκόμοις**, 'with their branches and leaves on,' lit. 'with their *very* branches,' etc., or 'branches, leaves, and *all*.' Cp. the use of *αὐτὸς* with a noun in the dative, as *αὐτοῖς ἀνδράσιν*, l. 656.

l. 632. **οὐδὲ κορύθων ἐδέοντο**. This may be an allusion to the fire which Pallas caused to blaze from the helmet of Diomedes, Hom. *Il.* v. 4:—

δαῖέ οἱ ἐκ κόρυθός τε καὶ ἀσπίδος ἀκάματον πῦρ.

These people, it seems, had it naturally.

l. 637, etc. Here Lucian gives us a very fair burlesque of descriptions of naval engagements, such as that in Thucydides, ii. 83–92, or the sea-fight in the harbour of Syracuse, *ib.* vii. 70, 71.

l. 640. **ἐμβληθεῖσαι**, 'struck in the side.' This mode of attack was properly called *ἐμβολή*, as distinguished from *προσβολή*, an assault prow to prow.

l. 644. **πολύποδας**. Aelian, *Varia Historia*, ch. i. describes the habits of the polypus, and its mode of lying in wait for and catching its prey (like the *pieuvre* or 'devil-fish' in Victor Hugo's *Toilers of the Sea*); Pliny, *Nat. Hist.* ix. 29, mentions an enormous one with feelers thirty feet long, which is doubtless an exaggeration of fact, as appears from the actual size of the octopus.

l. 649. **Αἰολοκένταυρος.** The *αἰόλος* in this compound probably means 'nimble,' as in the Homeric *πόδας αἰόλος*, etc. **Θαλασσοπότης** of course is 'Sea-drinker,' from *ποτὸς* (*πίνω*).

l. 656. **αὐτοῖς ἀνδράσιν.** Cp. l. 626, n.

l. 660. **τῶν ὀγδοήκοντα,** 'eighty *in all*,' lit. '*the* eighty' made up by computing the whole sum.

l. 664. **ἐξάψαντες αὐτοῦ τὰ ἀπόγεια,** 'fastening their hawsers to it.'

BOOK II.

l. 1. **μηκέτι.** Here the *μὴ* may have its usual subjunctive form, '*feeling* that I could not bear,' etc. But we cannot be sure that it is not another instance of Lucian's free use of this particle. Cp. i. 24, n.

l. 11. **τοῦ καύματος,** genitive of respect = 'the creature continued insensible to the heat.' Cp. *εὖ ἔχειν*, *κακῶς ἔχειν*, etc.

l. 14. **ἀπενενέκρωτο,** 'it had mortified.'

l. 17. **κινδυνεύσομεν,** the ind. for the opt. in a dependent clause. Cp. i. 163, n.

l. 22. **ἀραιωμάτων.** Cp. i. 457, n.

l. 33. **πᾶν ἐπάγη,** etc., perhaps in the allusion to the account in Herodotus, iv. 28, of the sea freezing about the Palus Maeotis (Azov), so that waggons are driven over the ice. Cp. Ovid, *Trist.* iii. 10, 29. Lucian knew nothing of the real frozen sea, and thought that lighting a fire on the ice (l. 39) was an impossibility.

ἐξεπιπολῆς, i.e. *ἐξ ἐπιπολῆς*, 'on the surface.'

l. 51. **ὁ Μῶμος,** etc. Momus, the critic of the gods and their doings, is mentioned by Hesiod, *Theog.* 214, as the son of Night. He is the personification of censorious ridicule (*μομφή*, from *μέμφομαι*). Hence his name passed into a sort of proverb, *οὐδ' ἂν ὁ Μῶμος τὸ τοιοῦτον μέμψαιτο*, Plato, *Rep.* vi. ch. 2. This piece of criticism about the bull's horns is referred to by Lucian in his *Nigrinus*, *ἐκεῖνος ἐμέμφετο τοῦ ταύρου τὸν δημιουργὸν θεὸν, οὐ προθέντα τῶν ὀφθαλμῶν τὰ κέρατα.* In the *Jupiter Tragoedus* and *Concilium Deorum* Momus is introduced as the utterer of some home truths about the gods at the celestial conclave.

ll. 58, 61. Note the pun in *Galatea* from *γάλα*, and *Tyro* from *τυρός*. For the real Galatea, beloved by Polyphemus, see Theocritus, *Idyll* xi. Tyro was said to have been visited by her lover Poseidon in the form of the river-god Enipeus, Hom. *Od.* xi. 235, etc.

l. 62. **μετὰ τὴν ἐντεῦθεν ἀπαλλαγήν**, some translate 'after her departure from her country' (Thessaly), or 'after Poseidon had left her.' But it seems to mean simply 'after her death.'

l. 75. **Φελλώ.** There was a real Phellos in Lycia. Cp. Liége in Flanders, by which word M. De Beauchamp renders Φελλὼ here.

l. 87. Cp. Hdt. iii. 113, *ἀπόζει δὲ τῆς χώρης τῆς Ἀραβίας θεσπέσιον ὡς ἡδύ.*

l. 89. **ἀμπελάνθης** = *οἰνάνθης*, the flower of the wild vine, from which a perfume was made.

l. 95. **μουσικά**, 'musical,' the later sense of the word. Properly *μουσική* meant literature and the fine arts generally, in which 'music' was included. Cp. *μουσικὰ ἀκούσματα* in the passage quoted from the *Axiochus*, in the note on l. 170.

l. 99. **διεσάλευον**, 'kept stirring.' The *διὰ* probably denotes *continued* action.

l. 100. **ἀπεσυρίζετο**, lit. 'were produced like whistling,' i.e. 'the branches when stirred gave forth a pleasant whistling sound.'

l. 101. **ἐπ' ἐρημίας**, *in loco deserto.* Another reading is *ἐπ' ἠρεμίας*, *leniter.* The expression may refer to the shepherds' custom of hanging up their pipes as an offering to Pan in a solitary place, where the wind would blow through them, as through an Aeolian harp. Cp. Virg. *Ecl.* vii. 24 :—

'Hic arguta sacra pendebit fistula pinu.'

The *πλάγιος αὐλὸς*, or *πλαγίαυλος*, is the 'cross-flute,' *flauto traverso*, formerly called the 'German' flute, which is held horizontally and played by means of holes at the side, being in fact what we now call simply the 'flute.' The other kind was known as the *flûte à bec*, played by a mouth-piece at the end, of which our 'flageolet' is the only existing specimen.

l. 112. The Isles of the Blest are described by Pindar in his Second Olympian Ode, ll. 70, etc.—

ἔνθα μακάρων νᾶσος (acc. pl.) *ὠκεανίδες*
αὖραι περιπνέοισιν, ἄνθεμα δὲ χρυσοῦ φλέγει,
τὰ μὲν χερσόθεν ἀπ' ἀγλαῶν δενδρέων, ὕδωρ τ' ἄλλα φέρβει,
ὅρμοισι τῶν χέρας ἀναπλέκοντι καὶ κεφαλὰς
βουλαῖς ἐν ὀρθαῖς Ῥαδαμάνθυος.

l. 115. The madness of Ajax, inspired by Athenè, whereby his fury was diverted from Odysseus and the other chieftains upon the flocks and herds, forms the subject of the *Aias* of Sophocles.

l. 119. Hellebore was supposed to be an antidote for madness. Cp. Aristoph. *Vespae*, 1489, where the slave Xanthias bids his master *πῖθ' ἐλλέβορον.* Hence the proverb, originally in Hor. *Sat.* ii. 3. 166, 'naviget Anticyram,' where the hellebore grew.

l. 120. Hippocrates, the physician of Cos, flourished about 430 B.C.

l. 122. Theseus had carried off Helen when a girl, aided by Pirithous of Athens. After her release by Castor and Pollux she returned to Sparta, and married Menelaus.

l. 127. **τὴν Ἀμαζόνα,** Antiope. The daughters of Minos were Phaedra and Ariadne.

l. 128. In the 12th Dialogue of the Dead Alexander and Hannibal dispute for the precedence. At the suggestion of Scipio, Minos adjudges the prize to Alexander.

l. 141. **προθεσμίαν.** Cp. i. 568, n.

l. 143. **αὐτομάτων,** etc. A close imitation, perhaps intended as a parody, of Xenophon's dream, *Anab.* iv. 3. 8, where the fetters which bound him seemed 'to slide off of their own accord' (*αὐτόματοι περριρυῆναι*). Cp. Acts xii. 17.

ll. 145, etc. Some have seen in this description a reference to the New Jerusalem of Rev. xxi, xxii. It may be a mere coincidence. The Greek poets would supply most of the materials, and we do not know that Lucian was acquainted with the New Testament or any part of the Scriptures. Still the *ἄμπελοι δωδεκαφόροι* in line 172 have, it must be confessed, an exact parallel in Rev. xxii. 2. See Introduction, pp. xviii, xix.

l. 153. **πηχέων βασιλικῶν.** Herodotus, i. 178, says 'the royal cubit exceeded the common cubit by three fingers' breadth,' making about 1 ft. 10 in. according to Professor Rawlinson's calculation in his note on the passage.

ll. 159, etc. Lucian has been supposed to be ridiculing Plato's theories concerning the nature of the soul, as set forth in the *Phaedo* and elsewhere. But Plato distinguishes between good and bad souls; only the latter retain the form of the body and are contaminated by it, while the former become pure and immaterial, *οὐδὲν τοῦ σώματος ξυνεφέλκουσα* (*Phaedo*, ch. 29). The satire is directed rather at the popular notion of the spirits of the dead as shadowy human forms, according to the descriptions in Homer and Virgil.

l. 163. **οὐκ ἂν ἐλέγξειε,** 'he would never discover.' **Ἐλέγχειν** is properly to refute an assertion by proving its contrary.

l. 164. ὀρθαί, 'erect,' i.e. as it were, lifted up from the ground.

l. 170. Cp. the following description in the *Axiochus* (a dialogue attributed to Plato) of the 'Land of the Leal' (*εὐσεβῶν χῶρος*)—*παντοῖοι λειμῶνες ἄνθεσι ποικίλοις ἐαριζόμενοι, καὶ κύκλιοι χοροὶ* (l. 204), *καὶ μουσικὰ ἀκούσματα . . . οὔτε γὰρ χεῖμα σφοδρὸν οὔτε θάλπος ἐγγίγνεται, ἀλλ' εὔκρατος ἀὴρ χεῖται.*

l. 176. **Μινῴου,** formed after the analogy of Asiatic names of months (with which Lucian must have been familiar), e.g. *Hermaeus, Metrous,* etc. in Bithynia, *Aphrodisius*, *Caesarius*, etc. in Cyprus. The Athenian months were not, except Poseideon, named after gods or heroes, but marked the seasons for various occupations, as Gamelion, Elaphebolion, etc.

The whole description (from l. 170 onwards) reads like an exaggerated imitation of Homer's account of the gardens of Alcinous, *Od.* vii. 114, etc., where fruits of all kinds grew in never-failing succession, ripened by a perpetual west-wind at all seasons of the year.

l. 194. **μουσικὰ ὄρνεα.** Cp. l. 95, n.

l. 196. **καταυλίφει** should be *καταυλίφουσι*, since the subject is *ἀηδόνες καὶ τὰ ὄρνεα*, but the singular verb is owing to the *neuter* plural immediately preceding.

l. 201. It appears from this and other passages that Lucian had a real respect for Homer, notwithstanding what he had said about him in his preface, i. 32.

l. 205. **Eunomus** was a harp-player of Locri in the south of Italy. A story of him is told by Clement of Alexandria, how once in a musical contest in summer time Eunomus broke a string of his lyre; whereupon a grasshopper that had been chirping near sprang upon the neck of the instrument and sang as upon a branch. The minstrel, adapting his strain to the grasshopper's song, made up for the want of the missing string. According to Strabo, a statue of Eunomus with the grasshopper and the lyre was erected at Locri.

Arion is said to have been the inventor of 'dithyrambic' poetry, a kind of high-flown lyric strain, originally in honour of Bacchus. He is best known in connexion with the story of the dolphin, related by Herodotus, i. 24, and by Ovid in the *Fasti*, ii. 83, etc.

l. 206. **Anacreon** of Teos flourished about 530 B.C. The festive odes now extant in his name are confessedly spurious.

Stesichorus, of Himera in Sicily, is said to have been blinded by Castor and Pollux for writing scurrilous verses against Helen, and to have recovered his sight on composing a *Palinodia* or retractation of the satire.

l. 211. **ἐπαυλεῖ**, 'plays an accompaniment,' properly on the flute (*αὐλός*). The trees are the orchestra on which the winds play; hence they are said *κατάρχειν*, 'to lead' the music.

l. 219. **Λοκροῦ Αἴαντος.** The Locrian or Lesser Ajax, (so called to distinguish him from Ajax, son of Telamon, l. 311,) was the son of Oïleus, Virg. *Aen.* i. 41. He is said to have assaulted Cassandra in the temple of Athenè, who slew him with the thunderbolt of Zeus. Homer, *Od.* iv. 499, etc., represents him as having been wrecked on the Gyraean rocks by Poseidon for his insolent language to the gods.

l. 221. **Anacharsis**, the enterprising Scythian traveller, visited Greece and is said to have been taught by Solon. His countrymen (some say his brother) killed him on his return for introducing new ceremonies and customs (Hdt. iv. 76).

The following lines are preserved by Diogenes Laertius:—

> Ἐς Σκυθίην Ἀνάχαρσις ὅτ' ἤλυθε πολλὰ πλανηθεὶς
> πάντας ἔπειθε βιοῦν ἤθεσιν Ἑλλαδικοῖς,
> τὸν δ' ἔτι μῦθον ἄκραντον ἐνὶ στομάτεσσιν ἔχοντα
> πτηνὸς ἐς ἀθανάτους ἥρπασεν ὦκα δόναξ.

Zamolxis, or Zalmoxis (Hdt. iv. 95), is said to have been a Getan slave of the Samian Pythagoras. Having learnt from him the doctrine of the immortality of souls, he taught it to his Thracian countrymen, who worshipped him as the Good Spirit to whom they expected to go after death.

l. 222. **Νουμᾶν.** Numa Pompilius, to whom the Romans ascribed their laws and religion.

l. 223. **Phocion** was the leader of the peace party at Athens in the struggle against Macedon, and the principal opponent of Demosthenes on the question of war with Philip. He was distinguished for the uprightness of his policy, and became in high favour with Alexander. The Athenians accused him of treason, and put him to death, B.C. 317.

Tellus is mentioned in the *Charon*, ch. 10, as one ὃς εὖ τε ἐβίου καὶ ἀπέθανεν ὑπὲρ τῆς πατρίδος. In the celebrated discourse with Croesus, Solon assigned him the second place, according to Lucian, in respect of human happiness. Herodotus, i. 30, places him first. He died fighting bravely in a border war with the Eleusinians, and was honoured with a public funeral.

l. 224. **τοὺς σοφοὺς**, the Seven Sages, whose names are commonly given as Thales, Pittacus, Bias, Solon, Cleobulus, Periander, Chilon. But Plato, *Protagoras*, ch. 28, substitutes one Myson for Periander; hence perhaps his exclusion here by Lucian. Diogenes Laertius, §§ 40, 108, also mentions this substitution.

ll. 226, 227. The stories of Hyacinthus, accidentally slain by Apollo, and of Narcissus, who pined away for love of his own image, are told at length in Ovid, *Met.* x. 162, etc. and iii. 339, etc. That of Hylas is one of the Argonautic legends, see Apollonius Rhodius, *Argonautica*, ii. 1207, etc. It is the subject of the 13th Idyll of Theocritus, and is alluded to by Virgil, *Ecl.* vi. 43:—

> 'Hylan nautae quo fonte relictum
> Clamassent, ut litus *Hyla Hyla* omne sonaret.'

l. 229. **τὰ πολλὰ διήλεγχεν**, 'he was perpetually cross-questioning him.' The ἔλεγχος was a name given to Socrates' method of cross-examination, whereby he forced his opponent to contradict himself, and to confess his ignorance of the matter in dispute. The way he led men to argue with him was by assuming ignorance on his own part and professing to come simply as a learner. This was called his 'irony' (εἰρωνεία, l. 232). Lucian jocosely represents this 'cross-questioning' as the best proof of his affection for Hyacinthus. It was really so in the case of Alcibiades, who admits, in Plato's *Symposium*, that his intercourse with Socrates had done him more real good than the discourses of any statesman of the day.

l. 234. The allusion is to Plato's ideal State, as described in the *Republic*, in which 'philosophers' alone were to be the rulers.

l. 235. The Cyrenaic school of philosophy was founded about 370 B.C. by Aristippus, a disciple of Socrates, but luxurious and debauched in his habits, and in every way unworthy of his master. With respect to him therefore Lucian's satire is just, but not so as regards Epicurus. He started some sixty years later from the Cyrenaic dogma that Pleasure is the Chief Good, but he meant a refined intellectual pleasure, defined as φρόνησις, or practical wisdom, and ἀταραξία, or peace of mind. His followers however afterwards degenerated into gross sensuality.

l. 238. **ὅσα**, adverbial, 'just as,' or 'by way of.'

ὁ Φρύξ, to distinguish him from Aesop the Roman actor, a friend of Cicero. The slave Aesop is the author of the fables in prose, which are no longer extant, the so-called 'Aesopic' *prose* fables being spurious. But many of them were versified in Greek by Babrius and in Latin by Phaedrus.

l. 240. **Lais**, the celebrated Corinthian courtesan, really lived with Aristippus, for whom Lucian substitutes Diogenes, the founder of the Cynic or opposite school.

l. 243. **ἀρετῆς ὄρθιον λόφον.** The comparison of a virtuous life to the steep ascent of a hill, though adopted by the Stoics especially, appears first in Hesiod's *Works and Days*, ll. 285, etc. It was developed by Pythagoras, and is worked out at some length in an allegory known as *Cebetis Tabula*, ascribed to Cebes the friend and companion of Socrates, but probably of much later date. (See the Introduction to my edition of the *Tabula*, Clarendon Press Series, 1878). Hermotimus, in the Dialogue of that name, mentions Hesiod's allegory, saying that he has long been travelling along the road to Virtue's hill, but has only just reached the foot.

l. 244. **Chrysippus** was a disciple of Cleanthes the successor of Zeno, who founded the Stoic school. In taking him as the representative of the Stoics, Lucian may have had in mind the saying—

εἰ μὴ γὰρ ἦν Χρύσιππος, οὐκ ἂν ἦν Στοά.

In the *Vitarum Auctio* he makes Chrysippus say that no man can be a philosopher unless he takes a triple dose of hellebore. Cp. l. 119, n.

l. 246. **Ἀκαδημαϊκούς**, philosophers of the New Academy, represented by Arcesilaus (B.C. 240), and Carneades (about 160). Deriving from Plato the doctrine of the uncertainty of sense-impressions, but not accepting his peculiar solution of the difficulty, they became absolute sceptics, and differed more in name than in reality from the disciples of Pyrrho, who bore that title. They asserted the impossibility of a *criterion* or standard of truth, since neither reason nor sense can supply one; hence the allusion in l. 249, with a play on the word *κρίσις*,—i.e. if there be no *κριτήριον* there can be no *κρίσις*, and the office of Rhadamanthus would be a sinecure.

l. 252. **νωθείας**, 'torpidity,' 'laziness,' from *νωθής*.

μὴ has here its proper subjective force, '*feeling* that they could not reach it.' Cp. l. 1, n.

The scepticism of the Academicians was in fact a negation of all philosophy whatever, not an incentive to greater exertions, as in the case of Socrates and Plato.

ll. 259–273. Lucian touches superficially on three principal points of what is now famous as the 'Homeric Question;' first, Homer's origin and birth-place; secondly, the authorship of the poems and the genuineness of certain passages; thirdly, their design and the relation between the Iliad and Odyssey.

l. 260. The names of the seven cities, each of which claimed to be the birth-place of Homer, are given in the well-known lines—

'Smyrna Chios Colophon Salamis Rhodus Argos Athenae,
Orbis de patria certat, Homere, tua.'

By pushing his birth-place so far eastward as Babylon, Lucian reduces the question to an absurdity, and is possibly jesting at the theory of one Alexander of Paphos, who made Homer an Egyptian.

l. 261. **νομίζουσιν**. Cp. i. 163, n.

l. 263. **ὁμηρεύσας**, a playful way of settling the meaning of the name *Ὅμηρος*, as if = 'hostage.' Its derivation is still a matter of dispute. It is supposed to be from the root ὁμ- in *ὁμ-οῦ*, etc. and *ἄρ-ω*, i.e. 'the fitter' or 'composer;' or more probably in a passive sense 'the fitted' or 'united,' in reference either to the union of various lays in one poem, or to the mingling of different grammatical forms and dialects. The traditional explanation was that *ὅμηρος* meant 'blind' in the Cymaean dialect of Aeolia. Cp. Milton, *Paradise Regained*, iv. 259—

'*Blind* Melesigenes, thence *Homer* called.'

l. 265. **ἀθετουμένων**, 'regarded as spurious.' Zenodotus, and after him Aristarchus, both of Alexandria, made recensions (*διορθώσεις*) of Homer's text, and rejected a great many passages. Lucian accuses them of bad taste in so doing.

l. 266. **καὶ ὅς**. Cp. i. 157, n.

l. 268. **ψυχρολογίαν**, 'coldness,' i.e. 'dullness' of appreciation. Cicero, in his treatise *De Claris Oratoribus*, speaks of a 'genus acuminis in reprehendendis verbis, nonnunquam *frigidum*.'

l. 270. **τῆς μήνιδος**, 'the wrath' of Achilles, with which the Iliad opens. This may mean either—why did Homer make this the starting-point of his Epic? in other words, is the poem an original 'Achilleid,' afterwards enlarged (Grote, *Hist. of Greece*, chap. xxi.)? or why did he begin with the word *μῆνιν* rather than any other word? This would be a hit at the 'micrologists,' as they were called, who fancied some hidden mystery to be couched in almost every word of the poem.

l. 271. **μηδὲν ἐπιτηδεύσαντι**, i.e. without any special object such as the 'micrologists' imagined. Lucian does not mean to say that Homer wrote without any care or idea of connexion in the several parts of his poem.

l. 272. **εἰ προτέραν ἔγραψε**, etc. This is also a modern question. In favour of the commonly received order, the marks of higher civilisation in the Odyssey, its more coherent structure, and certain peculiarities of language have been chiefly relied upon. Mr. Grote in his 21st chapter inclines to the opinion that both poems belong to about the same age, and hesitates as to the priority of the Iliad. Lucian does not mention the *Chorizontes* or Separatists, who assigned each poem to a distinct author. This theory, originated by one Xenon and adopted by Hellanicus, found a strong opponent in Aristarchus (l. 265, n.). It does not seem to have excited much attention at the time, which is probably the reason why Lucian ignores it.

l. 274. **οὐδὲ τυφλὸς ἦν.** The belief in Homer's blindness is of very ancient date. Cp. l. 263, n. It is asserted in the Homeric Hymn to Apollo, quoted by Thucydides, iii. 104, as genuine, but now known to be spurious:—

τυφλὸς ἀνήρ, οἰκεῖ δὲ Χίῳ ἐνὶ παιπαλοέσσῃ.

l. 280. **ὕβρεως**, not the strict legal term for insulting *language* or 'libel,' which was called *λοιδορία* or *κακολογία*. *Ὕβρις* was wanton injury to the *person*, such as formed the ground of the famous action brought against Midias by Demosthenes, B.C. 355.

For **Thersites**, 'the ugliest man that came to Troy, halt of foot, crook-backed and peak-headed,' and his treatment by Odysseus, see *Iliad*, ii. 212, etc.

l. 284. **ἑπτάκις ἀλλαγεὶς**, etc. According to the 'Transmigration' theory of Pythagoras, souls were believed to inhabit different bodies for certain successive 'periods' of time. Pythagoras asserted that he had himself undergone four or five such transmigrations, the second being that into the body of the Trojan Euphorbus (l. 286), who was slain by Menelaus. He is said to have proved the fact by taking down at first sight the shield of Euphorbus from the temple where it was dedicated. To this Horace refers, *Odes*, i. 28. 11, 'clipeo Trojana refixo tempora testatus.'

l. 285. One of the fables about Pythagoras was that he had a golden thigh. In the *Vitarum Auctio* or *Sale of Philosophers*, the purchaser of Pythagoras exclaims—'By Heracles, his thigh is all gold! Surely he is a god and not a man! I will certainly buy him.' Here Lucian improves on the legend by making him half golden.

l. 289. Upon the alleged death of Empedocles by throwing himself into the crater of Aetna, Diogenes Laertius records the following satirical lines :—

Καὶ σύ ποτ', Ἐμπεδόκλεις, διερῇ φλογὶ σῶμα καθήρας
πῦρ ἀπὸ κρητήρων ἔκπιες ἀθανάτων,
οὐκ ἐρέω δ' ὅτι σαυτὸν ἑκὼν βάλες ἐς ῥόον Αἴτνης,
ἀλλὰ λαθεῖν ἐθέλων ἔμπεσες οὐκ ἐθέλων.

l. 295. **Κᾶρος ὁ ἀφ' Ἡρακλέους.** Nothing is known of him. Some think Lucian invented the name and pedigree to puzzle the critics. It may be remarked, as a curious coincidence, that the name of Carus a Roman poet occurs in Ovid, *Epist. ex Ponto*, iv. 16, in connexion with that of Hercules (a poem he wrote bearing that title) :—

'Et qui Junonem laesisset in Hercule Carus,
Junonis si non jam gener ille foret.'

l. 297. **Areus**, a philosopher of Alexandria, who with his two sons, Dionysius and Nicanor, instructed Augustus in philosophy (Suetonius, *Octavius*, ch. 89). According to Quintilian, iii. 1. 16, he was also a writer on rhetoric.

l. 298. **Epeus**, the son of Panopeus, won a boxing-match against Euryalus at the funeral games in honour of Patroclus, Hom. *Il.* xxiii. 664.

l. 301. Plutarch tells a story of a contest between Homer and Hesiod at Chalcis, in which Hesiod won the prize, it was said unfairly. There is a composition still extant, *Certamen Homeri et Hesiodi*, written about 100 A.D., and suggested by the above-mentioned story. Hesiod is commonly supposed to have lived about a century after Homer.

l. 306. The story of Phalaris (B.C. 570) and his brazen bull is well known. In the two pieces entitled *Phalaris*, Lucian defends the tyrant against the common charge of cruelty. There was in fact a later tradition, which represented him as a mild and just ruler, forced into severe measures by occasional necessity, and especially as a patron of arts and literature. The celebrated *Epistles of Phalaris*, though proved to be spurious, are an evidence of this belief.

l. 307. **Busiris** is said to have sacrificed strangers, but to have been slain by Hercules, an intended victim. Herodotus, ii. 45, discredits the story, omitting however the mention of Busiris by name.

l. 308. **Diomedes**, king of the Thracian Bistones, fed his mares on human flesh. To capture these mares and to slay their master was one of the Twelve Labours of Hercules. Euripides, *Alcestis*, 481, makes Heracles call at the house of Admetus on his way to this adventure—

Θρῃκὸς τέτρωρον ἅρμα Διομήδους μέτα.

Sciron, a robber who infested the Attic frontier of Megara. Sinis, called Πιτυοκάμπτης, or the 'Pine-bender' (see Lexicon), pursued the same occupation on the Isthmus of Corinth. Both are said to have been slain by Theseus.

l. 311. **Αἴας ὁ Τελαμώνιος.** Cp. l. 115, n.

l. 314. Socrates fought as a hoplite at the battle of Delium, B.C. 424. His orderly retreat amid the general confusion is described in Plato's *Symposium*, ch. 36; how he marched along 'calmly surveying his friends and his foes, so that it was plain to all that if any one attacked him he would resist stoutly.' Lucian makes his present superiority consist in the fact of his not fleeing at all, as if he could have done anything else at Delium under the circumstances. See Thucydides, iv. 96, where however Socrates is not mentioned, a fact which led Athenaeus, *Deipnosophistae*, § 216, to discredit the story of his having been present.

l. 319. **Νεκρακαδημίαν** is of course a hit at Plato's Academy for *living* disciples.

l. 326. A parody of the first line of the Odyssey. The satire lies in the word νεκύων attached to ἡρώων.

l. 328. **τὰ ἐπινίκια.** sc. θύματα, the accus. of cognate or equivalent meaning with εἱστιῶντο. Cp. δαίνυσθαι δαῖτα and similar expressions in Homer, or (more precisely) δαίσομεν ὑμεναίους, 'the nuptial feast,' Eur. *Iph. in Aulide*, 123.

l. 331. **μυσαττόμενος τὴν κυαμοφαγίαν.** Pythagoras forbade his disciples to eat beans. No one knew why, and no Pythagorean would reveal the secret. All sorts of absurd reasons were suggested; some are enumerated by Diogenes Laertius in his Life of Pythagoras. Pliny gives the common-sense reason that bean diet is heavy and engenders dullness, but he also mentions a superstitious belief that the spirits of the dead reside in beans. Two verses ascribed to Pythagoras run thus:—

Δειλοί, πάνδειλοι, κυάμων ἄπο χεῖρας ἔχεσθε·
ἶσόν τοι κυάμους τε φαγεῖν κεφαλάς τε τοκήων.

Hence arose a saying that a Pythagorean would as soon eat his father's head as eat a bean. In one of Lucian's *Dialogues of the Dead*, Pythagoras asks Menippus what he has in his wallet. 'Beans,' says Menippus, 'which are not for you to eat.' 'Ah!' replies Pythagoras, '*nous avons changé tout cela*; beans and parents' heads are not the same thing down *here*, I find.'

l. 339. **ἀμηχανίας,** 'distraction,' not knowing what to do with himself. Cp. *Philopseudes*, § 14, ἀμηχανῶν τῷ ἔρωτι.

l. 355. **ἀσφοδελίνην**, the derivative adj. of ἀσφόδελος, for which see Lexicon.

l. 359. **παρὰ τοσοῦτον**, etc., 'so near they were to escaping,' lit. 'to so small a distance they came of escaping,' παρὰ denoting motion to get near an object. Cp. *Cataplus*, § 4, παρὰ τοσοῦτον ἦλθε διαφυγεῖν. Also with the genitive, as παρὰ τοσοῦτον ἡ Μιτυλήνη ἦλθε κινδύνου, Thuc. iii. 49. Cp. παρ' ὀλίγον, l. 613.

l. 366. **ἐμπροθέσμους**, within the time of the προθεσμία (l. 141), i.e. before the allotted time had expired. The opposite is ἐκπρόθεσμος. Cp. *Hermotimus*, § 80, ἐκπρόθεσμον τοῦ ὀφλήματος, 'over the due time for paying the debt.'

l. 372. **τοὐπιὸν**, 'the future' (τὸ ἐπιόν). Cp. Eur. *Alc.* 173, τοὐπιὸν κακὸν, 'the coming fate.'

ll. 375, etc., suggested by Circe's instructions to Odysseus, *Odyssey*, xii. 37, etc.

l. 377. **ἐπανόδου**, 'return home.'

l. 384. **ἐναντίαν**, etc. Cp. τὴν ἀντιπέραν, l. 689. The ancients had a vague notion of a large continent or island far away to westward, where America actually is. This was sometimes described as the island of Atlantis, very fruitful and populous, and larger than Asia and Africa combined. Aristotle *De Mundo* speaks of countries at a vast distance off and opposite (ἀντιπόρθμους) to ours. In Aelian's *Varia Historia*, iii. 18, Silenus the Satyr is represented as holding a conversation with Midas. He tells him that Europe, Asia, and Africa are islands bounded by the Ocean stream, and that the only existing continent is 'outside of the world' (ἔξω τοῦ κόσμου); an immense tract of land with gigantic inhabitants, whose strange customs he proceeds to describe. It is to this or a similar belief that Lucian here alludes.

l. 386. **ἀμίκτοις**. Cp. i. 542, n.

l. 388. **μαλάχης ῥίζαν**, suggested by the herb μῶλυ, which Hermes gave Odysseus (*Od.* x. 305) to keep him from harm. Cp. Milton's *Comus*, 636.

ll. 391, 392. A satire on the σύμβολα or mystic injunctions of Pythagoras, e.g. 'not to stir the fire with a sword, not to step over a yoke or sit on a quart measure, and to abstain from certain food, especially beans' (l. 331, n.). The first was explained to mean 'not to provoke the wrath of potentates' (δυναστῶν ὀργὴν μὴ κινεῖν) and similar mystic interpretations were given of the rest. Mr. Collins, in his *Lucian* ('Ancient Classics' Series) compares the old burlesque oath sworn by travellers at Highgate, 'never to stir the fire with a sword, nor to kiss any woman above two-and-twenty.'

l. 405. For the island of Ogygia, see Hom. *Od.* i. 85.

l. 406. **Ναύπλιον**, an actual name in mythology, given to the legendary founder of Nauplia on the Saronic gulf.

l. 412. **ὁμιχλώδης**, 'misty,' from *ὀμίχλη*.

l. 417. **ἀπόξυρος**, 'precipitous,' from *ἀπο-ξέω* = *ἀπότομος*, *abruptus*.

l. 424. **ποταμοὶ**, etc. Lucian probably had in mind the description in the *Phaedo*, ch. 60, of the rivers in Hades, 'some of fire, others of mud, like the lava streams in Sicily, which move up and down by a sort of oscillation inside the earth. One of these rivers falls into a vast space burning with fire and forms a lake boiling with water and mud; this they call Pyriphlegethon.'

l. 425. **ἀπέρᾱτος**, 'impassable' (*περάω*).

l. 429. **λυχνίσκους**, perhaps may be rendered 'lampreys,' or 'lamp-*rays!*'

l. 430. **Timon**, the Athenian misanthrope, is the subject of one of Lucian's most effective dialogues.

l. 434. **περιηγηταὶ**, 'guides,' from *περιηγέομαι*.

l. 438. **Κτησίας**. Cp. i. 22, n. Herodotus has several times already been the butt of Lucian's satire.

l. 440. This may be in a sense true, after the frank avowal in i. 46.

ll. 445, etc. An enlargement (with improvements) upon Homer's description of Dreamland, with its two gates of horn and ivory, whence issue true and false dreams respectively. See *Odyssey*, xix. 562, etc.; Virg. *Aen.* vi. 894, etc.

l. 453. **μηδὲ** should be *οὐδὲ*, as stating a fact. Cp. i. 24, n.

l. 457. **μανδραγόραι**. Cp. *Timon*, § 2, *καθάπερ ὑπὸ μανδραγόρᾳ καθεύδεις*. The 'mandrake' is a narcotic plant allied to the deadly nightshade. Cp. Shaksp. *Othello*, iii. 3, 'Not poppy nor *mandragora* . . . shall ever medicine thee to that sweet sleep, which thou owedst yesterday.'

l. 459. **ὄρνεον**. Lucian probably did not know that the bat is *not* a 'bird.'

l. 460. **Νυκτιπόρος**, 'Nightfare.'

l. 461. **Νήγρετος**, 'Wakeless,' or 'Neverwake.' Cp. *νήγρετος ὕπνος*, Hom. *Od.* xiii. 80.

l. 464. Cp. *Od.* xix. 562:—

> *δοιαὶ γάρ τε πύλαι ἀμενηνῶν εἰσὶν ὀνείρων·*
> *αἱ μὲν γὰρ κεράεσσι τετεύχαται, αἱ δ' ἐλέφαντι.*

l. 465. **Βλακείας πεδίον**, 'the plain of Indolence.' (Francklin.)

l. 470. **Νυκτῷον**, 'temple of Night,' formed like **Λητῷον**, *Ἑρμαιον*, etc.

l. 475. **Ταραξίωνα**, etc. 'Trouble-wit, son of Vain-hope and Purse-pride, son of Cut-a-dash.' This last rendering may represent the notion of empty display suggested by *Φαντασίων*.

l. 477. **Καρεῶτιν,** 'Sleep drench,' (Tooke,) from *κάρος*, 'torpid slumber.'

l. 479. The name Antiphon, meaning the 'answerer' (*ἀντί-φωνος*), indicates his office of interpreter of dreams.

l. 487. **ἐς βασιλέας,** 'like kings.' Εἰς, lit. 'into' another state or condition, denotes conformity or likeness. So *ἐν*, as *ἐν ἄνδρασιν*, 'in fashion of men,' Eur. *Alc.* 723. Cp. the French *en*, as 'voyager *en* prince,' etc.

l. 490. **ὡς ἄν,** = 'as though,' *quasi*. Cp. i. 76, n.

ll. 505, etc. For the building of the skiff on Circe's island, see *Odyssey*, v. 234, etc. Afterwards Odysseus is wrecked by Poseidon (*ib.* 315), and saved by Leucothea or Ino, daughter of Cadmus (*ib.* 332). His arrival at the Phaeacian land is related at the end of the same Book.

l. 509. The massacre of the suitors forms the subject of the 22nd Book, entitled Μνηστηροφονία.

l. 510. Telegonus, being sent by Circe to seek his father, was wrecked on the coast of Ithaca, and proceeded to ravage the country. Odysseus, not knowing who he was, went out to oppose him, and was slain by his son. This story is told in the *Telegonia*, a continuation of the *Odyssey*, and the last poem of the 'Epic Cycle,' written by Eugammon about 560 B.C.

l. 512. Cp. *Od.* v. 135, where Calypso says to Hermes concerning Odysseus :—

τὸν μὲν ἐγὼ φίλεόν τε καὶ ἔτρεφον, ἠδὲ ἔφασκον
θήσειν ἀθάνατον καὶ ἀγήρων ἤματα πάντα.

l. 517. **ταλασιουργοῦσαν.** *Ib.* 56 :—

ἡ δ' ἔνδον ἀοιδάουσ' ὀπὶ καλῇ
ἱστὸν ἐποιχομένη χρυσείῃ κερκίδ' ὕφαινεν.

l. 522. In l. 216 of the same Book, Odysseus calls Penelope by the simple epithet *περίφρων*, but does not otherwise extol her virtues to Calypso.

l. 532. **ξηρανθῶσι,** sc. *αἱ κολόκυνθαι*. from the adj. *κολοκύνθινα* in the preceding line. Observe the change from plural to singular in *αὐτήν*, i.e. '*one* of them.'

l. 533. **ἐντεριώνην,** 'the inside' of the pumpkin.

l. 535. **ἀπὸ,** 'with,' of the instrument. Cp. Dem. *Philipp.* i. *ἀπὸ τῶν ὑμετέρων ὑμῖν πολεμεῖ συμμάχων*. **Δύο** is often undeclined.

l. 542. **ἐν τοσούτῳ,** 'at this juncture,' stronger than *ἐν τούτῳ*. Lit. 'on so great,' i.e. 'so favourable' an opportunity.

l. 549. **ἀπεκρύψαμεν.** See special meaning of *ἀποκρύπτω* in Lexicon.

l. 553. **ἐπὶ δελφίνων,** in allusion to the common stories of dolphins carrying men on their backs, e.g. that of Arion, Hdt. i. 24. Gellius quotes a tale of a dolphin that carried a boy on his back every day from Baiae to Puteoli.

ll. 562, etc. The reader will remember the story of the Roc and its egg in the Second Voyage of Sinbad the Sailor. Whether Lucian may have borrowed from the Arabian Nights (or rather from the common material out of which those tales were composed) is a fair question. See Introduction, p. xvii.

l. 570. The Chian wine-jar held some three or four quarts of our measure.

l. 576. χηνίσκος. Greek ships had the extremity of the prow shaped like a goose's or swan's neck, hence the name. See *Dict. of Antiquities*, under Navis.

l. 584. Lucian's satire is directed at the common superstition, which saw in every strange occurrence an omen of divine anger, requiring prayer or sacrifice to avert it. See Virg. *Aen.* ii. 680-700, for one instance out of many.

l. 588. καταπεφυτευμένον, 'thickly set.' The *κατὰ* has its intensive force, as in *καταφαγεῖν*, *καταφθείρειν*, etc.

l. 591. χρῆ, the indic. for the opt. in 'graphic' narration. Cp. i. 163, n.

l. 601. ἀνιμησάμεθα. Cp. Xen. *Anab.* iv. 2, 8, *ἀνίμων ἀλλήλους τοῖς δόρασι.*

l. 606. This is possibly a real line of Antimachus, perverted by Lucian in its application. Antimachus of Colophon, about 400 B.C., wrote a *Thebaid*, several lines of which are cited by Athenaeus; also some elegiac poems. The emperor Hadrian is said to have preferred him to Homer.

l. 612. διαχωρίσματα, 'clefts,' from *διαχωρίζω*.

l. 613. παρ' ὀλίγον. See note on *παρὰ τοσοῦτον*, l. 359.

l. 615. εἱστήκει, etc. Some see in this a scoffing allusion to the passage of the Red Sea by the Israelites. But see note on l. 145, and Introd. p. xix. note 3.

l. 626. For the Minotaur, the offspring of Pasiphae and the Cretan bull and guardian of the labyrinth, see Virg. *Aen.* vi. 24–30 (' mixtum genus, prolesque biformis Minotaurus,' etc.). Perhaps the Βουκέφαλοι are intended as a burlesque of the *Cynocephali* or dog-headed inhabitants of India, mentioned by Ctesias. Cp. i. 22, n.

l. 629. πλὴν, = ἀλλά, 'except that.' Cp. i. 237, n.

l. 635. περιϊδεῖν. Cp. i. 303, n.

l. 649. συμπεφύκεσαν. The augment is sometimes omitted in the pluperf. even by the best Attic prose writers. Cp. *γεγένητο* in Thucydides, *πεπόνθειμεν*, *πεφύκει*, etc., in Plato, *προκεχωρήκει*, *τετελευτήκει*, *ἀποδεδράκει*, etc., in Xenophon.

l. 666. **Καβαλοῦσα, Ὑδαμαρδία.** No satisfactory explanation has been given of these names. The first looks like a participle of *κατα-βάλλω* (= Καββαλοῦσα), qy. '*Downing* island'? The second perhaps should be Ὑδραμαρδία, and may refer to the *water* transformation described below, l. 685.

ll. 668-676. A parody of Homer, *Od.* x. 317, etc., where Odysseus defends himself against Circe's enchantments with the *moly* which Hermes had given him, draws his sword upon her, and forces her to disenchant his crew. The 'bones and sculls' (l. 670) may have been suggested by the description of the Sirens' coast, *Od.* xii. 45:—

πολὺς ἀμφ' ὀστεόφιν θὶς
ἀνδρῶν πυθομένων, περὶ δὲ ῥινοὶ μινύθουσιν.

l. 678. **Ὀνοσκελέας.** Cp. the fabled Empusa, a spectre sent by Hecate to devour men, also called ὀνοσκελὶς and ὀνοκώλη.

l. 685. **ὕδωρ ἐγένετο.** This was one of the transformations of Proteus. Cp. Virg. *Georg.* iv. 410, 'aut in aquas tenues dilapsus abibit.'

l. 689. **τὴν ἀντιπέραν.** Cp. l. 384, n.

l. 697. **ἐξενηξάμεθα** = ἐξενεύσαμεν. Νήχομαι is a less common form for νέω.

l. 704. **ἐν ταῖς ἑξῆς βίβλοις**, etc. This promise appears never to have been fulfilled. One of Lucian's French translators, Perrot d'Ablancourt, has added a very tame continuation of the story, written by his nephew.

INDEX

The references are to the Notes and to the pages of the Introduction.

Academic school of philosophy, ii. 246; p. xx.
Adjectives in -ιος of two or more terminations, i. 116.
Aesop, the fabulist, ii. 238.
Age of Lucian compared with that of Socrates. pp. xii, xiii.
Ajax, his madness, ii. 115.
— the Locrian, ii. 219.
Alexander, the false prophet, pp. x, xviii.
ἀμέλει, sense of, i. 103.
ἂν, rare use of with fut. indicative, i. 47.
Anacharsis, the Scythian traveller, ii. 221.
Anacreon, the Teian, ii. 206.
Antimachus of Colophon, ii. 606.
ἀπὸ, instrumental use of, ii. 535.
Arabian Nights, whether known to Lucian, ii. 562; p. xvii.
Areus, the philosopher, ii. 297.
Arion, mention of, ii. 205.
Article, predicative use of, i. 26, 75.
ἀρχὴν = *omnino*, i. 51.
Augment omitted in pluperfect, ii. 649.
αὐτοῖς ἀνδράσιν, i. 656.

Baron Münchhausen compared with the *Vera Historia*, p. xxiii.
Béquet's French version of the *Vera Historia*, i. 54; p. xxiii.
Busiris, the Egyptian, ii. 307.

χρῆσαι and χρήσασθαι, i. 373.
Christianity, how far satirised by Lucian, pp. xviii, xix.
Chrysippus, the Stoic, ii. 244,
City of the Blest, Lucian's account of, p. xviii.
'Cloud-cuckoo Town' of Aristophanes, i. 430
'Cognate' accusative, ii. 328.
Colossus of Rhodes, i. 280.
Comparison of primitive adverbs, i. 607.
Ctesias, his History of India, i. 22, ii. 438, 626; p. xvii.
Cyrenaics, allusion to, ii. 235.

Diomedes, the Thracian, ii. 388.
Dolphins, stories about, ii. 553.
Double superlative, i. 91.
Dreamland, Homer's description of, ii. 445.
δόξαν, construction of, i. 95.
δύο, undeclined, ii. 535.

ἑαυτὸν, denoting the 1st or 2nd person, i. 72.
εἰ for ὅτι, i. 41.
εἰς, peculiar force of, ii 487.
ἐλέγχειν, ii. 163.
ἐμβάλλειν, a naval term, i. 640
ἐμοὶ δοκεῖν and similar phrases, i. 87, 467.
Empedocles, physical theory of, i. 377.
— story of his death, ii. 289
Empusa, fable of, ii. 678.
ἐνδιδόναι, special meaning of, i 439.
Endymion, legend of, i. 158.
Epicurus, satirised by Lucian, ii. 235.
ἐπὶ, denoting a condition, i. 311.
ἐπιδιδόναι, special meaning of i. 69.

ἐτετάχατο and similar forms, i. 193.
Eunomus, story of, ii. 205.

Flutes, different kinds of, ii. 101.

Galatea, ii. 58.
Gardens of Alcinous, in Homer, ii. 176.
Genitive, partitive, i. 249.
— of time, i. 538.
γοῦν, explanatory force of, i. 4.

Hellebore, an antidote for madness, ii. 119, 244.
Herodotus, allusions to by Lucian, i. 221, 340, ii. 33, 87, 438.
Hill of Virtue, allegory of in Hesiod, i. 243.
— *Cebetis Tabula*, ib.
Homer, his alleged blindness, ii. 274.
— supposed contest with Hesiod, ii. 301.
'Homeric Question' as discussed by Lucian, ii. 259, etc.
Homerus, meaning and derivation of, ii. 263.
Hyacinthus, story of, ii. 226.
Hylas, story of, ii. 227.

Iambulus, alluded to by Lucian, i. 25; p. xvii.
ἰδιώτης, secondary meaning of, i. 37.
Iliad and Odyssey, their order and comparative age, ii. 272.
Indicative for optative in dependent clauses, i. 163, ii. 17, 261, 591.
Island of Atlantis, ii. 384.
Isles of the Blest, described by Pindar, ii. 112.
ἱστορία, original and derived senses of, i. 30.

καὶ = ὅτε, i. 90.
καὶ δή, i. 152.
καινὸς and νέος, i. 31.
κατὰ with accus., special force of, i. 142.

Lais of Corinth, ii. 240.
'Land of the Leal,' ii. 170.
Lucian, his early life and travels, pp. ix, x.
— — Greek style, p. xi.
— — later years, p. xi.
— — *Dialogues of the Gods* and *of the Dead*, pp. xii, xiii.
— — satires on the philosophers, p. xiv.
— — social satires, p. xv.
— — relation to Christianity, pp. xviii, xix.
— — style and manner of his fiction, pp. xx, xxi.

Mandragora, or 'mandrake,' ii. 457.
μὲν οὖν, i. 543.
μή, proper use of, i. 10, 385.
μὴ for οὐ, frequent use of by Lucian, i. 24, 50, 503, ii. 1, 453; p. xi, note.
μὴ in indirect questions, i. 270.
Minotaurus, mention of, ii. 626.
Momus, references to, ii. 51.
Months, Greek names of, ii. 176.
μουσική, original meaning of, ii. 95.

Narcissus, story of, ii. 226.
Naturalness of Lucian's fiction, i. 180; p. xxi.
New Jerusalem, supposed reference to by Lucian, ii. 145; pp. xviii, xix.

ὁ and ὃς, old demonstrative use of, i. 157, ii. 278.
Ocean-stream of Homer, i. 54.
Odysseus, killed by Telegonus, ii. 510.
Ogygia, Calypso's island in Homer, ii. 405.
Optative, denoting frequent action, i. 152, 476.
Originals of the *Vera Historia*, real or supposed, pp. xvi, xvii.
ὡς ἄν, elliptic use of, i. 76.
ὡς δή, ironical force of, i. 29.
ὤφελον, expressing a wish, i. 252.

Parasites and hired dependents, p. xv.
παρὰ τοσοῦτον, meaning of, ii. 359.
Peregrinus, his mock martyrdom, p. xix.
περιορᾶν, meaning of, i. 303, ii. 635.
Phalaris, the tyrant, ii. 306.
Philopseudes, a dialogue, p. xvi.
Phocion, his policy, ii. 223.
Pillars of Hercules, i. 54.
Plato, his Republic, ii. 234; p. xx.
πλὴν = ἀλλά, i. 237, ii. 629.
Pluperfects, use of by Lucian, i. 511; p. ix, x, note.
Plural verb with noun singular, i. 186, 220.
Polypus, or octopus, description of, i. 644.
προθεσμία, technical sense of, i. 568.
Pythagoras, his mystic injunctions, ii. 391.
— Transmigration theory, ii. 284; p. xx.
— fable about, ii. 285.
Pythagoreans forbidden to eat beans. ii. 331.
φθάνειν, construction of, i. 456.

Quevedo's *Visions*, p. xxii.

Rabelais, compared with Lucian, i. 406; p. xxii.
Rivers of Hades, ii. 424.
Roc, story of in Arabian Nights, ii. 562; p. xvii.

Satire of Lucian, its real object, p. xiv.
Sciron, the robber, ii. 308.
Seven Sages of Greece, ii. 224.
Shepherds' pipes, dedicated to Pan, ii. 101.
Sinis, the 'Pine-bender,' ii. 308.
Socrates at the battle of Delium, ii. 314.
— his cross-examining method, ii. 229; p. xx.
Spirits of the dead, popular notions about, ii. 159; p. xx.
Stesichorus of Himera, ii. 206.
Subjunctive for optative, i. 576.
Swift's *Gulliver's Travels*, p. xxii.

Tellus, the happiest of mankind, ii. 223.
Thersites, mention of, ii. 280.
Timon of Athens, ii. 430.
Translations of the *Vera Historia*, p. xxiii.
Tyro, legend of, ii. 61

ὕβρις, a legal term, ii. 280.

Vera Historia, modern continuation of, ii. 704.
— general account of, pp. xvi–xxi.
— modern imitations of, pp. xxii, xxiii.
Voltaire's *Princess of Babylon* and *Micromegas*, p. xxii.

Western continent, ancient notion of, ii. 384.

Zamolxis, worship of, in Thrace, ii. 221.

THE END.

ADDENDUM

Jerram's Greek Text on p. 13 has suffered a censorship appropriate, perhaps, for his original Victorian audience of young students. However, there is absolutely nothing here that would shock today's reader who is of college age or older. On p. 13, lines 331-2, Jerram's Greek reads that Endymion, King of the Moon, promised to give "his daughter" in marriage to the narrator. In fact, the original Lucian says that the king promised to give "his son", since there were no women on the Moon, a thing he had neglected to tell us!

The subsequent deletion by Jerram is a lengthy passage. In the manner of modern science fiction, the narrator talks of the strange sexual biologies and mores of the inhabitants of the Moon. Quoted here from the Loeb Classical Library text, this passage should be cross-referenced to p. 13, line 335, of this book. The vocabulary is at the level of the small Liddell-&-Scott and any really controversial ideas should be handled at the discretion of the individual instructor.

καὶ ὁ μὲν ἠξίου με[1] μεῖναί τε παρ' αὐτῷ καὶ κοινωνεῖν τῆς ἀποικίας, ὑπισχνούμενος δώσειν πρὸς γάμον τὸν ἑαυτοῦ παῖδα· γυναῖκες γὰρ οὐκ εἰσὶ παρ' αὐτοῖς. ἐγὼ δὲ οὐδαμῶς ἐπειθόμην, ἀλλ' ἠξίουν ἀποπεμφθῆναι κάτω ἐς τὴν θάλατταν. ὡς δὲ ἔγνω ἀδύνατον ὂν πείθειν, ἀποπέμπει ἡμᾶς ἑστιάσας ἑπτὰ ἡμέρας. 22

Ἃ δὲ ἐν τῷ μεταξὺ διατρίβων ἐν τῇ σελήνῃ κατενόησα καινὰ καὶ παράδοξα, ταῦτα βούλομαι εἰπεῖν. πρῶτα μὲν τὸ μὴ ἐκ γυναικῶν γεννᾶσθαι αὐτούς, ἀλλ' ἀπὸ τῶν ἀρρένων· γάμοις γὰρ τοῖς ἄρρεσι χρῶνται καὶ οὐδὲ ὄνομα γυναικὸς ὅλως ἴσασι. μέχρι μὲν οὖν πέντε καὶ εἴκοσι ἐτῶν γαμεῖται ἕκαστος, ἀπὸ δὲ τούτων γαμεῖ αὐτός· κύουσι δὲ οὐκ ἐν τῇ νηδύϊ, ἀλλ' ἐν ταῖς γαστροκνημίαις· ἐπειδὰν γὰρ συλλάβῃ τὸ ἔμβρυον, παχύνεται ἡ κνήμη, καὶ χρόνῳ ὕστερον ἀνατεμόντες ἐξάγουσι νεκρά, θέντες δὲ αὐτὰ πρὸς τὸν ἄνεμον κεχηνότα ζῳοποιοῦσιν. δοκεῖ δέ μοι καὶ ἐς τοὺς Ἕλληνας ἐκεῖθεν ἥκειν τῆς γαστροκνημίας τοὔνομα, ὅτι παρ' ἐκείνοις ἀντὶ γαστρὸς κυοφορεῖ. μεῖζον δὲ τούτου ἄλλο διηγήσομαι. γένος ἐστὶ παρ' αὐτοῖς ἀνθρώπων οἱ καλούμενοι Δενδρῖται, γίνεται δὲ τὸν τρόπον τοῦτον. ὄρχιν ἀνθρώπου τὸν δεξιὸν ἀποτεμόντες ἐν γῇ φυτεύουσιν, ἐκ δὲ αὐτοῦ δένδρον ἀναφύεται μέγιστον, σάρκινον, οἷον φαλλός· ἔχει δὲ καὶ κλάδους καὶ φύλλα· ὁ δὲ καρπός ἐστι βάλανοι πηχυαῖοι τὸ μέγεθος. ἐπειδὰν οὖν πεπανθῶσιν, τρυγήσαντες αὐτὰς ἐκκολάπτουσι τοὺς ἀνθρώπους. αἰδοῖα μέντοι πρόσθετα ἔχουσιν, οἱ μὲν ἐλεφάντινα, οἱ δὲ πένητες αὐτῶν ξύλινα, καὶ διὰ τούτων ὀχεύουσι καὶ πλησιάζουσι τοῖς γαμέταις τοῖς ἑαυτῶν. ἐπειδὰν δὲ γηράσῃ ὁ 23 ἄνθρωπος, οὐκ ἀποθνῄσκει, ἀλλ' ὥσπερ καπνὸς διαλυόμενος ἀὴρ γίνεται. τροφὴ δὲ πᾶσιν ἡ αὐτή· ἐπειδὰν γὰρ πῦρ ἀνακαύσωσιν, βατράχους ὀπτῶσιν ἐπὶ τῶν ἀνθράκων· πολλοὶ δὲ παρ' αὐτοῖς εἰσιν ἐν τῷ ἀέρι πετόμενοι· ὀπτωμένων δὲ περικαθεσθέντες ὥσπερ δὴ περὶ τράπεζαν κάπτουσι τὸν ἀναθυμιώμενον καπνὸν καὶ εὐωχοῦνται. σίτῳ μὲν δὴ τρέφονται τοιούτῳ· ποτὸν δὲ αὐτοῖς ἐστιν ἀὴρ ἀποθλιβόμενος εἰς κύλικα καὶ ὑγρὸν ἀνιεὶς ὥσπερ δρόσον. οὐ μὴν ἀπουροῦσίν γε καὶ ἀφοδεύουσιν, ἀλλ' οὐδὲ τέτρηνται ᾗπερ ἡμεῖς, οὐδὲ τὴν συνουσίαν οι παῖδες ἐν ταῖς ἕδραις παρέχουσιν, ἀλλ' ἐν ταῖς ἰγνύαις ὑπὲρ τὴν γαστροκνημίαν· ἐκεῖ γάρ εἰσι τετρημένοι.

THom

THOM

THom

STUDENT'S NOTES